— First Edition —

A Promise Given

Books by Rick Steber

Rendezvous
Traces
Union Centennial
Where Rolls the Oregon
Heartwood
Oregon Trail – Last of the Pioneers
Roundup
New York to Nome
Wild Horse Rider
Buckaroo Heart
No End in Sight
Buy the Chief a Cadillac
Legacy
Forty Candles
Secrets of the Bull
Caught in the Crosshairs
A Promise Given
Red White Black
All-Around and the 13th Juror
A Better Man
Three Little Birds

Tales of the Wild West Series
Oregon Trail
Pacific Coast
Indians
Cowboys
Women of the West
Children's Stories
Loggers
Mountain Men
Miners
Grandpa's Stories
Pioneers
Campfire Stories
Tall Tales
Gunfighters
Grandma's Stories
Western Heroes

www.ricksteber.com

RICK STEBER

A Promise Given

A True Story of Life, Love...and Bluebirds

TWO STAR

Published by – *TWO STAR* –
An imprint of Bonanza Publishing
PO Box 204
Prineville, OR 97754

Cover design by Gary Asher
Book design by Jody Conners
Bluebird art by Mary Marquiss

ISBN: 978-0-945134-40-4

PRINTED IN THE UNITED STATES OF AMERICA
FIRST EDITION

Dedication

To Vivian with love....

Note

When the first European settlers arrived on North American soil they were greeted by great flocks of friendly songbirds with lovely blue feathers. The colonists named the bird *blue robin,* and noticing the way they hunted insects in their gardens, orchards and fields, they erected bird houses on trees and wooden fence posts to encourage the birds to nest nearby.

Over the next two hundred years, the species that became known simply as *bluebirds* were driven to near extinction. Ninety percent of the bluebird population was killed. Many factors contributed to this staggering loss; the most apparent was triggered by one man, Eugene Schieffelin who took it upon himself to release into the United States all of the European birds mentioned in the works of William Shakespeare, including the house sparrow, bullfinch, chaffinch, nightingale and skylark. But it was his release of 60 starlings into New York City's Central Park in 1890 that caused the greatest damage. Starlings, aggressive by nature, drove the native birds from their traditional nesting sites and within a hundred years starlings had spread across the continent and their population had grown to more than 200 million. They are now listed as an *invasive species*.

Another cause leading to the decline of the bluebird population in America was the widespread use of DDT during the 1900s. This agricultural insecticide eliminated the food source of many birds and weakened their egg shells, making reproduction impossible. DDT became a rallying point for environmental awareness and in 1972 public pressure led to the banning of DDT in the United States. And finally, the bluebird population has suffered because modern development destroys sensitive areas and traditional nesting sites – urban sprawl, corporate farming practices and the replacement of wooden fence posts with steel T-BAR fencing.

The good news is, in the past few years the population of bluebirds appears to be on the rise, due mostly to bird lovers who have erected bird houses in safe locations and those in the agriculture community who are turning to alternative methods of pest control. If this trend continues, bluebirds will become a familiar sight and their clear, sweet songs will once again spill out over the hills and meadows. What can you do to help make this happen? Put up a bluebird bird house.

A Promise Given

A True Story of Life, Love...and Bluebirds

Bluebird Valley Ranch

~ Chapter One ~

My wife and I own a ranch in Eastern Oregon. We named it the Bluebird Valley Ranch and on this day, like most days when the weather cooperates, Vivian and I ride to the top of the ridge and sit there for endless hours doing nothing more productive than to enjoy the beauty of the landscape.

Off to the west the timbered Maury Mountains rise like folds and pleats on a thick, green blanket. The draws and canyons are defined by the changing leaves of aspen and cottonwood. Stands of tamarack in the process of dropping their needles show here and there as patches of soft gold. In all other directions the muted grays and tans and browns of the High Desert stretch to the far horizons. It is this rich beauty, and the vastness and solitude that we drink in with such gusto. We sit side-by-side, hips touching, watching a hawk ride the silent wind, or a black vulture curl in tight circles in a rising thermal. If we are lucky, and sometimes we are, a mountain bluebird flashes across our field of vision and Vivian is thrilled beyond words.

These days Vivian finds it difficult to talk. She more whispers than talks. I have to lean close to her lips to hear what she is saying. My hearing isn't so good. Damn this old age, but if you live long enough we all go through it, the slow deterioration of body and mind. We do if life does not come at us all at once and change in a heartbeat: we suffer a crippling stroke, a sudden brain aneurism, an incurable disease, even a car wreck. We know all too well about those things. Misfortune has struck our family many times over, and yet as we look out over the mountains and the desert we count our blessings.

Vivian sits beside me in a Kawasaki Mule, a four-wheel drive all-terrain vehicle. I have to strap her to the seat with a belt or she might fall out. She is that weak, and there are times the body tremors make her muscles spasm in uncontrollable fits. But I don't mind any of the hardships we face because, for all these years, Viv as I affectionately call her, has been my wife, my best friend, the mother of our four children and my Rock of Gibraltar. I don't know what I am going to do when she is gone. But let's not talk about that. Not now. Live in the moment. That is our motto. Live in the moment but believe in the past, our shared past.

One would think the yellow ball that is the sun should be warm but on this late fall day there is a harsh crispness in the air that lets you know winter cannot be far behind. Viv is wearing both a sweater and a coat. I had wrapped the scarf she once knit, back when her fingers were capable of doing such intricate things, around her neck and yet I see her shiver. At least I think it is a shiver and not a muscle spasm caused by the cruel Parkinson's disease that has so ravaged her body. I reach over, tuck the ends of the scarf inside and zip up her coat. She smiles at me. She loves me. I am a lucky man. I know that.

Could Viv have found a man more exciting than me? Probably. For 30 years I was an elementary school principal. I plowed a straight furrow through life. Never varied, never wandered. But then she knew that, what kind of man I was, going into our marriage. I was as steady and dependable as a work horse. That must have been what she wanted, a plodder she could count on and not some fancy, high-spirited thoroughbred that might have brought spectacular wins at the race track, but was just as likely to throw its rider and leave her crippled in its wake.

Because of her disease Viv wants me to do most of the talking. She likes it when I tell stories from my past, growing up like I did out in nature, or of my recollections of the events that define the life she and I have shared. I am writing these thoughts down so that in my old age I don't forget any of the splendid details. I know a few of my friends will read the words I write on these pages and proclaim, "Trevor, you've written yourself a goddamn love story." Others will read the same words and call it a tragedy every bit as heartbreaking and profound as Romeo and Juliet. I suppose it is a little of both. In life we are not blessed with sunshine every single day. Into life a little rain must fall. So love story, tragedy, you can take your pick.

What we really have here is the unfolding story of two very *common* people, common in most every way. In my opinion there is one thing and one thing alone that sets us apart and makes us unique and special. It is a very simple word, simple to say and yet extremely complex in its implications, and meanings, and emotions. That word is *love*.

Viv and I have shared love for nearly six decades, 58 years to be exact, and without reservation I can say our love, over time, has grown and blossomed and matured and today it is much deeper and more powerful than it ever was. It is love that resonates between us and intertwines our hearts and souls; a love that has brought us such a tremendous wealth of happiness. For me, that love is all I need to sustain me. That is everything.

Trevor Russell

"How the waiting countryside thrills with joy when Bluebird brings us the first word of returning spring... reflecting heaven from his back and the ground from his breast, he floats between sky and earth like the winged voice of hope."

– WL Dawson

Odell

~ Chapter Two ~

I'm a pretty reserved fellow, certainly not the type to toot my own horn, but since Viv was stricken with Parkinson's disease she likes for me to tell her stories about my upbringing, saying the way I was raised – pretty much in the sticks – is a window to my personality. I think her assessment is correct and believe that was one of the compelling reasons for us, after we retired, to buy a ranch 60 miles from the nearest town. All my life I have sought privacy and solitude and truly do take pleasure from being out in the wilds. I have to hand it to Viv, she was a town girl when I met her, but over the years she has grown to appreciate, as I do, all the simple pleasures of rural living.

Every night when Gordon Russell said his prayers, just before jumping into bed, he paused to ask God for one thing, to please bring him a brother. Twice his mother suffered miscarriages and then finally, when Gordon was 9 years old, in 1926, Trevor Russell was born. Gordon doted over his baby brother, and after a few years, when the little guy was able to get around, Gordon took him for walks in the woods, or fishing on Odell Creek.

There was no doubt Gordon loved his brother, but if the truth be known he probably loved to fish even a smidgeon more. He combined his two loves and dutifully took Trevor fishing, always at a good fishing hole where he parked the child, propping a rod up with rocks and setting a can of dirt and lively worms within easy reach. Gordon instructed his brother, saying, "Don't move from here. Stay away from the water. Watch the tip of your rod and if it twitches, if it so much as wiggles, set the hook and reel in your fish."

Having given these specific instructions, Gordon turned away and disappeared into the underbrush downstream, only to reappear hours later swinging a sagging forked willow stringer of silver-sided trout, big trout, way bigger than anything Trevor caught sitting at the fishing hole near the road.

And during those hours while Gordon was away Trevor dutifully sat as he had been directed, watching the tip of his rod and catching an occasional fish. But at some point Trevor always came to the realization he was alone. Sometimes he panicked, calling, "Gordon, where are you?" When there was no answer he cried hot tears and hollered, "Gordon, I'm scared." But Gordon never heard him, or if he did he ignored his little brother because a stringer of lunker trout was more important than placating his brother. Besides, Gordon was 9 years older than his brother and knew he wasn't going to be staying around home forever. Trevor had to learn to be confident on his own.

Trevor learned that his panic – yelling, pouting, tantrums and tears – never brought his brother back early. Gordon came back when he had caught his 20 fish bag limit. So Trevor had no choice but to adjust to being alone. He learned to relax and enjoy his surroundings; watching the yellow leaves turn loose their summer's grip and fall into the water, the way they twisted and twirled in the current. He observed the courtship of birds in the springtime, saw them drink from the stream or pick up twigs to build nests. Little by little Trevor's confidence grew until he felt okay being left alone, comfortable by a stream or in the deep woods. No longer was he a scared little boy dependant upon his big brother. And when that momentous awakening dawned on Trevor he became the one crawling through the tight underbrush, wiggling his way to the head of deep holes, fishing where the big trout lurked.

The Russell family lived on a small farm at the upper end of Hood River Valley, near the town of Odell, Oregon. The snowy white cap of Mount Hood was always present, looming only a few miles away to the southwest. Back in the late 1920s and '30s, the area was remote and inhabited by homesteaders with small orchards scattered across the valley floor. Trevor grew up fishing, hunting and camping. He had freedom to come and go as he pleased, and as long as he was back to the house at dinner time, or had told his parents in advance that he wouldn't be home, nobody seemed to care where he went or what he was doing.

*****

After Prohibition ended Frank Russell, who was always a bit of a plunger and could be enticed to jump into some risky venture if there was so much as a slight promise of a big payday, pulled up stakes in Odell and moved his wife and their two sons north. Frank had purchased a pool hall and beer parlor in Woodland, Washington. He operated the pool hall on his own and had his wife, Mildred, cook breakfast and make up sack lunches for the men working at the nearby sawmill. But when the Lewis River flooded in 1935 the pool hall was ripped from its foundation and floated away in the roily current, bobbing off down the river like a toy boat. After that fiasco Frank returned his family to the farm near Odell and took a job working for the orchardists as a cold storage engineer. He designed and built the facilities to keep fruit at the right temperature so it did not spoil and rot. He could do things like that, Frank could, using his intelligence and mechanical aptitude in conjunction with his skillful hands. Frank was a man who could accomplish most anything if he set his mind to doing it. At different times he was a barber, hard rock miner, orchardist, electrician, plumber, superintendent of a mine and a hired hand on ranches and farms.

*****

Trevor grew up on the farm near Odell. He was tall and as scrawny as a green bean that didn't get enough water to grow plump. When he started school the bigger boys teased him and although Trevor hated the teasing, he didn't put up much of a fight. He just flashed his tormentors a goofy grin and went about what he was doing. It was Gordon who didn't like the teasing. He was constantly standing up for his little brother and that made it all the worse because, when Gordon wasn't around, Trevor got picked on even more.

Gordon's gift to Trevor on his ninth birthday was two sets of boxing gloves and he showed him how they were to be used, teaching Trevor to cover up, sidestep punches, and how to open up and deliver quick combinations to vital spots on an opponent's body. He taught Trevor the art of boxing, coaching it was always best to go to the body, that once the opponent felt the sharp bite of leather to his exposed belly or ribs, the hands came down and the head would be exposed. And much to Gordon's amazement, he discovered his little brother loved to fight. Trevor was a natural, blessed with pure instinct and power and he didn't seem to mind getting hit if it allowed him to throw an even better punch. Before long Trevor was testing himself against his classmates, inviting them to swing by the house after school, where they strapped on gloves and went at it in the front yard. Nobody got seriously hurt but there were plenty of bloody noses, split lips, and on more than one occasion a boy went running home crying.

Gordon fancied himself a fighter and entered the Oregon Golden Gloves competition. The Russell family drove to Portland to witness the event. In his first fight Gordon had his opponent on the ropes, but because he felt sorry for his adversary he backed off and allowed the injured fighter to make it to the bell. In the second round Gordon was knocked down and counted out. The fight was over. On the way home Frank chided Gordon, saying emotion has no place in the ring and that a fighter has to have a killer instinct. Gordon never fought again, but Trevor learned from his older brother's mistake and any time he had a classmate hurt he kept throwing punches until his opponent called "Uncle!"

Frank was usually present to officiate these after school bouts. At the end of the evening, after Trevor had waded through his classmates, Frank invariably compared his son to Willie Pep, the World Lightweight Champion, saying if Trevor dedicated himself to the fight game and kept his nose clean, someday he would be a champion just like Willie Pep.

Going and coming to and from school Trevor passed Junior Moyer's house. Junior was a tough, snot-nosed kid who had an older brother even tougher. Trevor defeated Junior in a boxing match, fair and square, but Junior's older brother didn't subscribe to any rules of fairness. He jumped Trevor on his way home. Trevor came dragging into the house, bloody and dirty from getting rolled around in the road. Frank met him at the door, and once he heard what had happened, he told his son, "Here's what you do. Tomorrow he'll do the same damn thing. And he will keep after you day after day until you set him straight. Next time when he comes up to you don't wait, hit him on the point of the chin while he's relaxed. Get in the first punch and you'll take the fight right out of him."

The following day Trevor followed his dad's advice. The older Moyer boy stepped into the road and Trevor popped him, sending the bigger boy into his house bawling like a baby. After that Trevor never had a lick of trouble when he passed the Moyer house.

*****

Like everybody who lived through the Great Depression, times were difficult on the Russell family. Frank worked for the local orchardists when work was available, but it seemed as though apples, pears and cherries were considered a luxury item and not a necessity. Most folks could not afford a luxury and with little or no market for fruit, orchards were pulled out of production.

The only steady employment to be had was with President Roosevelt's Works Progress Administration (WPA), a federally funded program designed to put Americans back to work building roads and performing public works projects, mostly in the western states. Timberline Lodge on Mount Hood was built by the WPA, as was much of the Columbia River Highway.

Many nights Trevor lay awake in bed listening to his parents argue. His mom saw the WPA as an opportunity, and although she did not like the idea of her husband being gone all week and only home on weekends, she did like the idea of him having steady employment and receiving a monthly paycheck.

"I ain't interested," Frank emphatically stated each time Mildred broached the subject.

"Two bits an hour," countered Mildred, "Where else can you make two dollars a day? And foreman pays a dime more. Thirty-five cents. You have the experience to be foreman. If you apply they'll give you the job."

"Great," Frank stated. "Fine and dandy. I get to foreman a crew of slackers building toilets and laying slabs for footers. Outdoor shitters is what it's come down to. You want me to boss a crew of city kids fresh off the streets of New York, Chicago, Detroit and 10 of them will be leaning on shovels and one or two actually working. I don't have the authority to fire the slackers and everyone gets paid the same. Hells bells, we might as well embrace Communism and get it over with. That way we all get a free ride in the same sinking boat."

Mildred thought she was being reasonable. "At least we would have healthy food on the table."

This set Frank off. "You and the kids have never gone hungry; never missed a meal in your lives. You've always had fresh meat on the table."

And Mildred shot back, "If you call a steady diet of fish and poached venison meat on the table."

And that was the way the nightly discourse seemed to go in the Russell house, and similar conversations probably went on in many other houses across America. A woman wanted stability and money she could count on. A man stood firm on pride and refused to take a job he considered little more than a government hand-out.

Morning and night Frank and Trevor milked the family's two cows. Cream was separated, stored and sold on Saturday.

Skim milk was fed to the hogs. Milking one cow was about all Trevor could manage. By the time he finished stripping his cow his forearms were aching with fatigue.

"Trevor, there's something we need to discuss," said Frank one evening while they were milking. "Your momma wants me to go to work for the WPA and I don't want to do it. There are no jobs around here, none that pay decent. I got a job waiting for me in Woodland, Washington. All I have to do is get there. If I take it I can send home most of my paycheck. But son, I need your help. You're gonna have to take over the milking."

"Two cows," Trevor protested. "I can barely do one."

"Tell you what," said Frank. "Do this for me, milk both cows, and I'll give you an allowance of 50 cents a week."

Trevor didn't know any of his classmates who earned an allowance. He repeated, "Fifty cents a week."

"Payday every Friday. Go to a movie. Buy yourself a hamburger, school clothes, whatever you want. Your very own money. So what do you think of that?" Frank held out his hand to consummate the deal. Trevor took it. They shook.

The following morning Trevor faced two cows to milk. It was always two cows to milk and even when his dad came home on the weekends he never lifted a finger to help with milking. Two demanding cows robbed Trevor of time, time he could have spent fishing, hunting, camping or playing with friends. He soon came to view those cows as pitiful creatures, dirty and smelly and extremely demanding. Trevor had to get up early, go out in the cold and the rain and snow and get those two cows in, milk them and repeat the process again every evening. Never a day off. Never a break. Same routine, like the spinning of a wheel; at least a wheel on a car was getting somewhere. Trevor knew he was getting nowhere. He hated those cows, wanted them to die, and while he milked his forearms throbbed with the exertion and he imagined ways the cows might die – their heads stretched over the barbed wire fence when lightning struck, getting loose on the highway and a truck hitting them, drowning in the river.

One morning Trevor was stripping the last cow and she kicked, stuck her foot in the bucket and dented it. Trevor was late for school that morning. He came into the classroom and plopped down at his desk with an audible huff. Rosalie Jakku, a cute blonde that Trevor had a crush on and who sat directly behind him in class, tapped Trevor on his shoulder and whispered a question, asking him what was on his left arm. Trevor looked and to his complete embarrassment saw a wide swath of green cow manure smeared on the sleeve of his sweater. He bolted from the room, stripped off his sweater and cleaned it the best he could in the restroom. He swore vengeance against the offending cow. But that night he milked her just like he always did.

"Bluebirds are so pretty. The color of their feathers is true blue, and they're a very nice little bird. They are not mean or nasty."

– Bea Mansfield

The War

~ Chapter Three ~

From my point of view it would be best if I skip ahead in my story to when I met Viv and my life really started, but Viv will have none of it. She insists I tell it all – from my high school escapades to the outbreak of the war, the loss of my best friend because of that war, my service in the Air Force and even my first romantic love and the heartbreaking ending of that affair. When I tell that part of my story, Viv not having been my first, she says she might not have been my first, but by golly she will have loved me the longest. And when she says that she smiles and I know she loves me in a way no other woman ever has, ever will.

Sunday morning December 7, 1941 dawned clear and cold. Mount Hood stood gleaming under a fresh dusting of snow like a tall, white sentinel. Trevor finished milking and rather than do the homework he had been assigned over the weekend, he slipped out to try his hand at fishing. In early winter the fish are always hungry and within a couple hours he had caught his limit and returned home. When Trevor kicked off his boots in the mud room he heard Edward R. Murrow's voice on the radio speculating about what FDR's response would be and Trevor instinctively knew something big had happened in the world. A moment later his mother was there telling him the horrific news; the Pacific Fleet had been trapped at anchor in Pearl Harbor, many ships had been destroyed by bombs dropped from Japanese zeros and hundreds of United States sailors had been killed in the attack. The United States was at war with Japan.

Trevor laid his stringer of fish in the sink. He was not thinking about the events taking place far out in the Pacific, or the world now plunged into war, or even that he would soon be of the age to be drafted into the military and would likely have to fight in a war on foreign soil. His initial thought, his only thought, was for his best friend, his American Japanese classmate Tetsua Takasumi. This war was going to change everything and Trevor foresaw that Tetsua, born in Hood River and a citizen of the United States, was going to pay a far higher price than he ever would.

Trevor and Tetsua had grown up together, attending the same class in school. They shared common interests and had often fished, hunted and hiked into the woods with packs strapped on their backs. They carried sleeping bags, matches, a fry pan, and if they couldn't catch a fish, or shoot a rabbit or bird with their sling shots, they resorted to cooking bacon and potatoes over an open campfire. The potatoes never seemed to get done, not all the way through, but the boys ate them anyway.

In ninth grade Trevor had written a paper in social studies on the Japanese community in the Hood River Valley. He interviewed several Japanese and learned immigrants from

Japan first came to the Pacific Northwest in the 1880s to work on construction of the transcontinental railroad to Portland. They stayed to work on the Oregon Short Line and other railroads in the Northwest, and when the era of railroad building ended they became farm laborers, hoping to eventually own their own farms and orchards. Like many European Americans the immigrant Japanese saw independent farming as the way to move up the economic ladder. By 1910 the number of Japanese residents in the Hood River Valley numbered 468, almost 6 percent of the population. These immigrants leased farm land or bought the less desirable uncultivated land and struggled to clear that land and develop prosperous orchards and vegetable farms.

The Japanese erected a Community Hall in Hood River and established a Japanese Methodist Church in Odell. Christian and Buddhist congregations flourished. A Works Progress Administration (WPA) ethnology study found the older members of the Japanese community attempted to continue to preserve traditional celebrations, but the children of these immigrants spoke English and not Japanese and tried in every way to become Americanized.

After the bombing of Pearl Harbor – two soldiers from Hood River Valley were killed at Pearl Harbor – the young men began dropping out of school and joining the service. Anti-Japanese hysteria swept through the country, and throughout the Hood River Valley. Trevor worried Tetsua might be a target of classmates and others in the community. The wave of ill feelings against the "Japs" soon escalated to the point it was the common belief any person of Japanese descent posed a threat to the national security of the United States. The fear of many was that, after the demoralizing attack on Pearl Harbor and the destruction of the Pacific Fleet, the Japanese planned to mount an offensive attack against the West Coast and the Japanese living in the region would rise up and sabotage any resistance.

The federal government added to the public's panic by initially calling for Japanese Americans to voluntarily relocate from the Pacific Coast to the interior, but politicians such as Governor Chase Clark of Idaho vigorously opposed such a plan. He proposed, and had legislation passed, that effectively blocked Japanese families from purchasing land in Idaho. And whenever Trevor walked through Odell or Hood River with Tetsua, he heard the derogatory comments that were said behind their backs. He never discussed this with Tetsua. Teenage boys didn't talk about things such as racial discrimination, prejudice and bigotry. After all it was 1942 and they were just two kids who were way more alike than they were different, trying to get by with their homeland at war. Even Trevor felt the patriotic spirit and tried to join the Air Force. His mother refused to sign the papers saying he must graduate from high school, and then she would agree to allow her son to become a soldier and go off to war.

On February 19, 1942, President Franklin D. Roosevelt issued Executive Order 9066, which ordered the removal of 120,000 American Japanese from the Pacific Coast and their relocation to 10 inland camps located in isolated areas in seven western states. All Japanese living in the Hood River Valley were notified they were to be removed and relocated, and they were ordered to divest themselves of any personal property, or land, and immediately report to the Portland Assembly Center.

Tetsua called Trevor on the telephone to tell him of the President's order and say he was having to drop out of school and move to a relocation camp with his family. He told Trevor, "Come by the house tonight. I got something to give you."

When the boys met it was Trevor who was indignant. "What in the hell is the President thinking? This isn't right."

Tetsua was resolute. "We must follow orders. We have no choice."

The childhood friends stood facing each other. Neither could imagine Tetsua's fate: that he would live at the "Portland Assembly Center," a livestock pavilion with plywood walls scabbed together to make into rooms for families, a place that still smelled of cattle and pigs and sheep. From there, Tetsua and his family would be sent to the Tulelake Relocation Camp and forced to live in cramped barracks on a windswept sand flat, a dismal place with metal cots and straw for mattresses, where residents tried to reconstruct their lives behind barbed wire fences and in the shadows of guard towers. The imprisoned people rose above the harsh environment to grow flowers in the dry soil, form musical groups, publish a newspaper, play on sports teams and develop arts and crafts. They lived as prisoners, praying the end of the war would come soon.

"You speak English. You don't speak Japanese. You've never even been to Japan. You're a red-blooded American. Why can't FDR see that?" challenged Trevor.

Tetsua did not respond. Instead he turned to the bed where he had gathered the treasures of his life. His greatest of all was his hunting knife. He had saved to buy it. The knife was factory built with a stainless steel blade and a marble handle encased in a hand-tooled leather scabbard. Tetsua wore his knife whenever he was in the woods. And now he handed his knife to Trevor.

"I want you to have this," he said simply.

Trevor was unsure how to respond. He cleared his throat and managed, "I don't know."

"We can't have weapons," said Tetsua. "They'll take it away. You keep it."

Trevor now found it easier to speak. "Okay, but I'll give it back when you come home."

"It's yours. I don't know if I'll have a home to come back to," said Tetsua. "I'm enlisting as soon as I turn 16. If I'm overseas and get taken prisoner they'll kill me on the spot. I know that. You keep the knife. Just promise me, when you use it to gut a fish or cut a deer's throat, think of me."

"I will," said Trevor. He opened his belt and put on the scabbard and knife. When it was in place he stuck out his hand. Tetsua took it. White skin. Brown skin. And then they hugged. It was a brief coming together, arms slung around each other's shoulders loosely, a self-conscious pat or two, and then they parted. Trevor stepped away. "See you when I see you," he said and rushed from the room, plunging headlong down the short flight of stairs and outside into the cool night where the air was easier for him to breathe.

On the walk home that night Trevor thought about his friend up there in his room with all his worldly possessions scattered across his bed. He wished he had told Tetsua he would remember all those good times they had shared over the years, told him how much he valued their friendship, told him he loved him like a brother. Trevor felt ashamed he had said none of those things. The weight of the knife, scabbard firmly bound to his belt, slapped against his hip and leg with every step. Finally the tears came, searing tears that stung his cheeks like an unfair indictment. The war had claimed yet another casualty.

*****

Twenty-five years later Tetsua Takasumi would return to Odell for his class reunion. At the reunion dinner Trevor Russell was the master of ceremonies. He agonized over how to introduce Tetsua and other American Japanese, many whom had enlisted, served and fought for the United States in World War II. All had been uprooted, sent to relocation camps and not allowed to graduate with their classes. And so Trevor told a story; a story about how he and Tetsua, when they were in sixth grade, used to dig holes in the girls softball field behind the school, build fires, dump shotgun shells onto the coals and run and hide until the shells exploded. Trevor said, "I've often wondered if our pyromania, and desire to blow things up, is the reason the government rounded up Tetsua and the other American Japanese and shipped them off to Tulelake."

Everyone laughed. The passing years, the war that would never be forgotten – the bitterness and anger, shame and resentment – disappeared like vapor off a lake with the rising of the sun. Once again, they were classmates and nothing more.

*****

The summer of 1942 most able-bodied American men were away fighting wars on the Pacific and European fronts. There were not enough farm laborers to work the fields and orchards in the Hood River Valley. The local school board, along with most other school boards in the country, passed a resolution delaying the starting of school until the third week of October so children could be employed in the harvests.

With a long summer in front of him 15-year-old Trevor announced he was going to do his part for the war effort by working the pea harvest in Eastern Oregon. He hiked to the main highway, stuck out his thumb and caught a ride east toward Pendleton. He stopped in the town of Athena where he lived in a labor camp and worked in the pea harvest for 65 cents an hour. Upon receiving his first paycheck Trevor wrote his parents a letter and enclosed a five dollar bill. But he forgot to put a stamp on the envelope. When his mother was notified she owed for postage due, and saw the letter was from Trevor, she immediately worried her son had been unable to find employment and could not even afford a stamp to write home for money. She ripped open the envelope, discovered the five dollar bill and kissed it.

Trevor, after a month spent forking pea vines into a hopper, returned home to find the pickup truck pulled up tightly to the front porch and his father loading household furniture and boxes into the bed of the truck. When he spotted Trevor he shouted, "Lucky you got home when you did. We've sold the house and we're leaving in the morning." Frank went on to explain they were moving to the Mother Lode, a cinnabar mine in Central Oregon, where he had been hired as the superintendent. "The government needs quicksilver for making bombs. The mine has been shut down. We're reopening it."

In the morning Trevor was bouncing over the mountain roads, riding with his parents and all their household belongings. The Mother Lode was located on Lookout Mountain east of Prineville and the dirt road leading to the mine, a single lane with turnouts, was steep and full of switchbacks. At the top of the grade – Big Summit Prairie could be seen off to the east – they turned and followed little more than a trail to the mine. There was a cook shack and a boarding house and as workers arrived they were assigned bunks in the boarding house. Mildred, who had been hired to cook for the crew, went to work rustling up dinner.

Once the mine was reopened Trevor was hired on the crew and assigned to operating a jackhammer to loosen ore on the face wall. The ore was loaded into a cart and Trevor, all 135 pounds of him, was the designated donkey, pushing nearly a ton of oar along the slight downgrade to the entrance. He wore a hard hat with a carbide light affixed to it and nearing the entrance it was always a shock to him to come out of the dark and into dazzling sunlight slanting through the ponderosa pine.

When Trevor was not operating the jackhammer, or loading cars with oar and pushing them to the entrance, he assisted the powder monkey, Frank Coffman, drilling holes 4 feet deep into the wall face and stuffing the holes with dynamite. When a charge was ready to be blown the other miners exited the tunnel and the fan blowing fresh air into the shaft was turned off. One time Frank and Trevor were busy finding and lighting fuses and Frank had eight fuses burning but could not seem to locate the ninth and final fuse. Because of the lack of oxygen, Frank's light flickered and went out. Trevor said, "Don't worry about finding the last one. We've got to go."

"I'll find it," said Frank. "Give me your lamp."

Trevor handed over his lamp as he announced, "I'm getting out of here." He turned and scrambled down the tunnel, slipping in the darkness, blindly groping with his right hand to find the side tunnel he knew was there. He did find it and ducked inside, away from the blast that would surely come at any second. He crouched with his hands over his ears to muffle the roar of the explosion. He waited. And waited some more. Muffled footsteps were faintly audible. A weak light flashed across the tunnel floor. The roar of the dynamite exploding and a moving wall of concussion rushed down the narrow tunnel. Trevor was knocked off balance, fell against the hard rock wall and sucked in a quick breath that stung his nose and lungs from the sharp bite of burned explosives and thick, dry dust.

He pulled his shirt over his nose, drew another breath and was not at all sure if Frank had made it, or if he had been killed in the explosion. All Trevor was cognizant of was absolute darkness and an overpowering sense of isolation.

"Frank," Trevor muttered apprehensively, and then more boldly, "Frank!"

"I found it," replied Frank. "The last fuse. I found it." The force of the explosion had hurled Frank down the side tunnel. His light had been extinguished. He lay nearly at Trevor's feet. Together they made their way out of the dark mine shaft.

At supper that evening Trevor announced to his father that, after his birthday on Saturday, he planned to quit working in the mine, return to Odell and find a place to live. He said he wanted to graduate with his class. What he didn't say was, in his estimation, it was just too damn dangerous working alongside a crazy powder monkey like Frank Coffman, and if he continued on in the mine he was pretty sure he'd get blown to bits and die there.

Jeff, one of the miners at the table, paused halfway to his mouth with a generous spoonful of mashed potatoes and gravy. "Saturday's your birthday? How old you gonna be, kid?"

"Sixteen," replied Trevor.

Jeff wolfed down the bite and backhanded his mouth. He swallowed, and with a devilish grin and leaning so far back in his chair that the front two legs came off the floor, he announced, "In that case you deserve a treat. I'm gonna take you to Rosie's Cafe and buy you a meal you'll never forget."

Some of the other men at the table acknowledged Jeff's offer with grunts and knowing grins, but if Trevor's father caught on he never showed it. Trevor was absolutely oblivious. He protested, "You don't have to do that."

"Sixteen. You'll be a man," said Jeff. "There's no better place to celebrate the occasion than at Rosie's. You pick it out; whatever you want. My treat. So what you like?"

"Steak," said Trevor.

"Big, fat juicy steak," laughed Jeff.

For the remainder of the week, every time Jeff and Trevor passed in the tunnel or in the bunkhouse, Jeff rubbed his hands together and made some comment about the wonderful steak dinner Trevor was going to enjoy on his birthday, saying things like, "Wait until you sink your teeth into one of Rosie's finest," or "Rosie has the best meat this side of Portland," or "When you taste the meal Rosie serves you are gonna be spoiled."

Trevor never did catch on and come Saturday, after working at the mine until noon, Jeff and Trevor headed into town. Jeff wheeled his Chevrolet sedan into the parking lot at Rosie's Cafe, a nondescript building on the west side of Prineville near the Crooked River. They got out of the car and went to the front door. Jeff held open the door and Trevor stepped inside. The interior was dimly lit. Coming in from the summer sunshine it took a moment for his eyes to adjust. Trevor was soon able to distinguish tables and chairs scattered around the room. Against the far wall was a bar with colorful bottles lined up on shelves. But what really caught Trevor's attention were the waitresses. They stepped forward and made a line in front of him. There must have been seven or eight but they were not dressed like waitresses, not at all. They wore *skimpy* attire, *revealing* outfits that barely covered the essentials. The curves of their breasts, well-defined cleavage and thick, bare legs were exposed to view and Trevor's eyes widened. These women were much older than he was. They wore gaudy lipstick and red rouge powdered their cheeks. One woman had yellow hair and she licked her lips seductively, all but making her intentions obvious, but not to Trevor.

Jeff, from somewhere behind Trevor, asked, "What do you think?"

"I was just wondering," replied Trevor, "With so many waitresses, how this place could ever make any money."

There was laughter and Jeff announced in a loud voice, "Ladies this here rube is Trevor Russell. Today he turns sixteen. He's a virgin. Treat's on me."

The painted ladies rushed Trevor, grabbing at him, pawing him. He felt their plump breasts and eager flesh pressing against him and he panicked. He stumbled backwards, lost his footing and fell onto the floor. The ladies were around him and on him then. He could smell their strong perfume; feel the heat of their breath and their fleshy weight crushing against him. His reaction was to push them aside, leap to his feet and run like a scared little boy trying to outrun the boogeyman. And he heard them back there laughing, laughing at him, laughing and squawking like a tree full of raucous crows. He ran until he was gasping for breath and then he dropped to a steady walk. All he wanted was distance from those women. He chastised himself for being so naïve, so stupidly naïve. He walked uptown to the Horseshoe Tavern, went in, sat at the bar and drank a glass of beer like a man.

*****

Trevor's brother, Gordon, was attending Oregon College of Education. He wrote a letter inviting Trevor to come for a visit and Trevor diverted from his plans to return to Odell and wasted little time hitchhiking to Monmouth. He found Gordon living with four guys in a cabin sectioned off into bedrooms with thin plywood walls.

Gordon and his roommates occasionally studied, but mostly they drank beer, horsed around and played poker. Girlfriends came and went, stopping by to spend a few hours with their boyfriends and sometimes staying the night. One time a couple of girls dropped by and announced they were going to see the new Betty Davis film, "*Dark Victory.*" Since their boyfriends were away playing baseball they insisted Trevor accompany them to the show house. He eagerly complied and they sat near the front, Trevor between the two girls.

The movie was a tearjerker. Betty Davis's character, Judith, is a young, socialite/heiress with a passion for horses, fast cars and handsome men. She initially ignores brief episodes of dizziness and double vision, but when she falls off a horse she is taken to a specialist who conducts a series of diagnostic tests and his suspicions are confirmed that his patient has a malignant brain tumor. The doctor who operates on Judith promises a full recovery, but hides the fact the tumor cannot be completely removed and she will die within a year.

The doctor, of course, falls in love with Judith. They become romantically involved and are engaged to be married. But Judith discovers her case file, reads the truth, breaks off the engagement and returns to her previous life. One of her stable hands, played by Humphrey Bogart, who for years has loved her from afar, confronts her about her unruly behavior and she confesses she is dying. Their conversation convinces her she should spend her final months living with him. By the time the final scene rolls – Judith alone, lying on her bed and the image on the screen beginning to blur and eventually fading to a flat gray – the girls were gripping Trevor's arms and crying on his shoulders. Trevor enjoyed the sensations these older girls aroused in him and hated for the movie to end.

Trevor and the girls returned to the cabin. One of the girls went home but the other was so distraught she stayed to wait for her boyfriend. And that night Trevor laid face up in bed listening through the thin plywood walls as the girl told her boyfriend about the sad movie. Several times he heard the girl reprimand her boyfriend, "Stop it," and "You're not listening," and then she got to the ending and cried once again.

Her boyfriend consoled her. He said, "I want to touch you."

Trevor cupped his hands around his ears so he could hear better and thought he detected buttons slipping through button holes, clothes sliding off, the unhooking of a metal brassiere snap. Bed springs began squeaking rhythmically. Also audible were sighs and moans and more, way more. Trevor heard it all. And what made those suspended moments even more personal for Trevor was the fact this girl had been with him, had cried on his shoulder, held him tightly. He knew the smell of her perfume and how she felt when she had pressed against him. And now the girl in the bed a few scant feet away was having sex and Trevor did not dare draw a breath for fear he would miss some small nuance of her passion. He told himself someday he would have a girlfriend. And in time the bedsprings stopped singing their lyrical cadence and the distinctive sounds of lovemaking subsided. Yes, someday he would have a girlfriend.

*****

Trevor returned to Odell to start his junior year of high school. He found a place to live with a woman whose husband had gone to Alaska to work as a civilian for the Army. To pay his room and board Trevor milked two cows. Later that winter when the snow got too deep for travel to the mine, the Mother

Lode closed and Trevor's parents returned to Odell and rented a place. Trevor left the woman he was staying with and moved in with his parents. The subject of getting a milk cow did come up, but Trevor quickly vetoed the idea, claiming he had milked his last cow and wanted to have some fun before he graduated and went in the service. His father never again brought up the subject of cows.

*****

It was a moonlit Friday night in the dead of winter. A fresh storm was blowing in off the Pacific and clouds built against the Cascade Range and surged around Mount Hood like an incoming tide sweeping around a pier. The feathery edge of a windblown cloud reached out to touch the moon and then it passed and the white moon shown brighter than ever, illuminating skaters on a reflective sheen of ice. Nearby, a group of young people had gathered around a roaring bonfire.

Trevor was there, ice skates in hand, with his back to the fire. The fire was hot and yet Trevor could see the vapor of his breath when he exhaled into the cold night air. He turned to face the fire and that was when he saw her, saw Betty for the very first time. He stared transfixed. Heat shimmers danced and played with her image. She was young and beautiful. Trevor thought she was quite possibly the most beautiful girl he had ever seen. Her eyes were a lovely blue and her blond hair was long, cascading over her shoulders and framing the strong features of her face. Her cheekbones were high and well set. Lips full: no, her lips were plump. And the word that came to Trevor's mind to describe her straight, perfectly symmetrical nose was strangely enough, *adorable*. He had never in his entire life ever defined anything as *adorable*. Her skin, reflecting the soft red, yellow and pink hues of the fire, seemed almost delicate. This girl looked directly at Trevor and smiled. Her teeth were radiantly white and flawless. Trevor smiled back and was suddenly aware of a roaring in his ears like the whirl of wind inside a tornado. "Hi," he managed to say. "How are you?" He felt clumsy with the words he spoke.

"Good," she said. "The fire's hot."

Though their initial attempt at conversation was awkward they soon were less self-conscious and their words became more free-flowing. They skated together, holding hands, and at the end of the evening Trevor walked Betty home. On the way it snowed and the wind blew fiercely but Trevor never felt the cold. Actually there seemed to be a warmth radiating from somewhere in his body and he felt more alive than he had ever felt before. When they reached her door Trevor asked if he could see her the following day. Betty said yes.

Trevor did not own a car and on Saturday he walked with Betty and once more they talked. Betty was only in the eighth grade, although she said she was older than her classmates and should have been a freshman but was held back the year she had rheumatic fever. She said her folks owned the telephone company and she worked there after school. Trevor asked if he could come by the telephone office and watch her work. She said he could.

After that, almost every afternoon, Trevor went to the telephone office, sat in a straight-backed chair and watched Betty working as an operator. She wore a headset and pulled plugs and connected plugs. She spoke to customers and her voice was youthful, confident, sweet and pleasant; well suited for her exceptional good looks. Between customers Trevor and Betty visited about the progress of the wars in Europe and the Pacific. Trevor said when he graduated he was going to enlist in the Air Force and become a pilot. After the war he wanted to attend college and his goal was to someday become a teacher. Betty said she wanted to go to secretarial school, or beauty school, she wasn't quite sure yet.

Betty must have liked Trevor's easy charm. She said she did. He seemed to be exactly what she needed. He was funny and carefree, a gentleman almost to a fault, and he was confident about his future and what he wanted from life. She complimented him and said he was handsome and went on to say she enjoyed his intelligence and his drive to succeed. Her friends claimed Trevor had a reputation for being the best fighter in Odell and maybe the entire Hood River Valley. She didn't know about that. She had never seen him fight. She just felt safe and protected when she was with him.

It was weeks before Trevor got up the nerve to kiss Betty goodnight and when he finally did kiss her he wondered why it had taken him so long. And later, on a warm spring night on a blanket under an apple tree they both lost their virginity. In the aftermath of that stupendous event they talked about marriage, deciding they would wait until after she graduated from high school and after he returned from the war. They professed their love for each other and as summer progressed they oftentimes carried the blanket into the orchard and made love while the yellow sun or the ashen moon passed through green leaves overhead. They spent every stolen minute they could together. And when they were in public, at school, attending movies, going to dances, they were the picture-perfect couple. They looked good standing together. Trevor had broad shoulders, slender hips, a flat stomach and a tanned darkness to his skin from spending so much time in the outdoors. But then again, the winsome Betty would make anyone she was with look good. Trevor knew she could have any boy in school, or any man for that matter, but she loved him. She said she did and through Trevor's senior year, and Betty's freshman year, they only had eyes for each other. They had the ideal love, or so it seemed.

*****

The day after graduating from high school Trevor joined the Air Force. He was inducted at Fort Lewis, Washington and sent to school in Amarillo, Texas to train as a B-29 flight engineer. He believed he would soon be involved in the war; flying high over Germany or Japan, picking up flack from the ground like he saw on newsreels and dropping bombs on military targets.

Trevor was under the misconception that Texas, because it was so far south, was warm and the countryside was fertile and green. When he was sent there he was expecting sunshine, cowboys and cattle. Instead, on the first day Trevor was in Texas, the sun did shine and then the wind came up and blew in a dust storm. The temperature plummeted. A black cloud spit rain, sleet and finally hail. After all that the sun popped out and it got warm once again, until the sun dropped below the flat horizon and the cold returned forcing Trevor to pull on every sock he owned and still his feet were cold as he marched into a desert as flat and barren and uninviting as the alkali landscape east of Bend, Oregon.

After a 20 mile march Trevor's unit bivouacked and the men slept on the ground curled up in blankets, only to be awakened in the middle of the night and given orders to follow a compass course to a new bivouac site. The squad leader was a red-headed, college educated kid from back east who had book learning but very little common sense. It didn't take long for Trevor, who was used to hiking in the wilds, to realize their squad leader was lost.

"We're going in circles," announced Trevor.

"What makes you think so?" the kid from back east asked defensively.

"I watch the stars," said Trevor. "The north star, that one up there just off the lip of the Big Dipper, it doesn't move. Take a bearing off it and you'll know. And that hill over there, the one with the stair step cut, this is the third time we've walked past it tonight."

"I know what I'm doing," said the squad leader. "Follow me."

The unit did follow the squad leader until, while taking a compass reading, he set his rifle against a boulder. It was a good hour later before he realized he was not armed as all soldiers are required to be and went back after his carbine. In his absence the others asked Trevor if he thought he could find the bivouac site. With Trevor in the lead they hiked several miles, coming to a distinctive bowl-shaped valley that was described in the orders, where Trevor directed they should set camp.

The following morning the unit was commended for being closest to the bivouac site and the squad leader, who had found his carbine and caught up to his unit, took all the credit despite the fact every soldier knew it was Trevor who deserved the accolades.

*****

The West Texas Regional Golden Gloves Tournament was held in Amarillo and Trevor, who had been told all his life by his father that he would be a champion in the ring just like Willie Pep had been, decided to enter the contest. There were 32 boxers in the lightweight division and Trevor, representing the United States Air Force, won his first four fights and was advanced to the finals. In that fight his opponent head-butted him, knocked loose several of Trevor's teeth, cut his lip and broke his nose. He was a bloody mess and tried to protest, but the referee wiped Trevor's face with a towel and told him, "Sonny, get in there and fight."

Trevor was mad at the referee and mad at his opponent. It was probably the only time in his life he had ever been mad to the point of rage. He came out swinging, decked the other fighter and claimed the victory. To commemorate the win he was given a miniature set of bronzed boxing gloves imprinted with the words, "Golden Gloves Lightweight Champion." Trevor sent the trophy to his father, along with a note that read, "Pop, you always said I would be a champion. Now I am. This is for you."

*****

Plainview, Texas was a dry town. It was illegal to sell or serve alcohol within the city limits. Every Saturday night a dance was held in Plainview, and because West Texas Teacher's College was located a few miles away at Canyon, there were always single girls available at those dances. This attracted the soldiers stationed in Amarillo and once they got to the dance they sought two things, a girl and something fortified to drink.

Trevor bought a 1942, model 45 Harley Davidson motorcycle and nearly every Saturday evening he made the run to Plainview to sell bootleg whiskey. He bought pint bottles, all he could fit into his saddlebags, paying a buck and a quarter in Amarillo and selling them at the dance for five. On a typical night Trevor ran out of booze long before he ran out of customers.

One time Trevor made the mistake of taking a buddy with him on the run. When they got to the dance Trevor's buddy was approached by a fellow who said he'd pay $20 for a bottle. When Trevor was introduced to the fellow he told the man,

"Well, if I hear of anyone selling whiskey I'll give you the high sign, but you know this is a dry town." The fellow offered $30. Again Trevor turned him down. "I'll let you know," he said and walked away.

"What the hell are you doing?" said Trevor's friend. "He offered thirty bucks. Why didn't you take his money?"

"Because," said Trevor, "it doesn't make sense for a man to offer six times the going rate. I figure he has to be a federal officer, or an undercover agent. If I sell him a bottle he's gonna turn around and arrest me."

Later, as Trevor and his friend were leaving town, they saw the customer who had wanted to pay $30 for a bottle. He was driving a police car. This incident convinced Trevor the authorities were onto his bootlegging operation and he never made another run.

On his frequent runs to Plainview Trevor had met and become friends with Mary, a college student. She was cute and sociable. They had danced together on many occasions and their friendship grew. Mary invited Trevor on a picnic. He picked her up on his motorcycle and she directed him up a winding canyon, telling him, "I know a secret spot."

Trevor parked at a narrow turnout. He packed the picnic lunch and Mary carried a blanket. They hiked to where a copse of pine trees grew in a tight circle around a miniature oasis of green grasses and delicate blue and yellow flowers. It was an idyllic setting, quiet and very secluded. Mary unfolded the blanket, spread it on the ground and lay down. She implored Trevor, "Come be with me."

Trevor stretched out on the blanket and immediately Mary rolled to him. She kissed him; a sensuous kiss, a kiss rich with meaning and promise. Trevor found it exceedingly difficult to pull away from her delicious lips, but he did: and when he did

Mary looked at him and whispered, "I want to give myself to you."

Trevor sat upright and crossed his legs Indian style. He contemplated exactly what it was Mary was offering. She wanted to have sex. If they did, he would know and she would know, but nobody else would ever be the wiser. It was an exciting temptation for Trevor. He could have Mary in this moment, in this little slice of heaven surrounded by a circle of trees. He felt the intoxicating tingle of temptation, but he also felt apprehension and guilt. Mary was a wonderful young woman; certainly pretty and smart. It was obvious she liked him. He watched her now, the way her breasts rose and fell with each quick breath she took. Her dress was riding high revealing long legs, incredible legs and he reached to stroke the exposed skin, skin that was soft and silky under his fingertips. His hand moved upwards a few inches more. He stopped and abruptly withdrew his hand.

"You can't do this can you?" asked Mary with genuine sadness. "You have a girl back home don't you? You love her."

Trevor nodded in confirmation.

"What's her name?" asked Mary.

"Betty."

"She must be very special."

"She is," said Trevor.

And that was the end of Trevor and Mary's romantic interlude. They ate their picnic lunch – fried chicken, beans and coleslaw – and Mary said if anything ever changed with Betty, Trevor should let her know. She admitted she had fallen in love with him and told him she had planned her picnic in the pines to consummate that love.

"But how could you?" asked Trevor. "We hardly know each other."

"It just happened," responded Mary.

*****

Trevor was given leave and wanting to see Betty he used the 10 days to hitchhike to Oregon. Upon reaching Hood River he surprised the love of his life by showing up at the telephone office and standing behind where she was seated at the bank of plugs. Betty sensed him there, turned, saw him and simultaneously threw aside the operator headphones, squealed with delight and flung herself into Trevor's open arms. She hugged and kissed him and cried a stream of happy tears. During his stay Trevor and Betty were able to spend one heavenly night in a motel room down by the river where they enjoyed the luxury of making love in a bed.

During the blissful time they were together Betty asked Trevor for a ring. He obliged, but instead of the engagement ring she was expecting he bought her a sterling silver *friendship* ring. He gave her the ring as he was preparing to leave, at a pullout alongside the Columbia River Highway. They kissed and vowed their undying love to each other and then Trevor got out and Betty made a U-turn in her parent's car and headed back to town. Trevor watched her drive away and when she was gone he stood in his Air Force uniform, duffel at his feet, and stabbed his thumb into the air.

*****

Trevor was given another leave at Christmas and this time when he arrived home he got down on one knee and proposed to Betty. She wept with joy as he slipped a beautiful engagement ring on her finger. "All my dreams have come true," she whispered to Trevor. "I'm so happy. You are the only man I ever want. I love you." And Trevor foolishly believed her.

They spent Christmas and New Year's Day together and then Trevor returned to Texas. Betty wrote him every day reminding him that as soon as the war was over they would be married. She had their life together planned and those plans included a small house in the Hood River Valley and two babies, a boy and a girl. She was dreamy with expectations.

*****

August 6, 1945 dawned bright and sunny, without a cloud in the Texas sky. The temperature soon was creeping toward a hundred degrees and Trevor was riding his motorcycle across the Air Force base in Amarillo, weaving his way through heavy traffic. Pandemonium suddenly broke out: horns honking and people shouting, yelling and whooping. A man in uniform, a captain as it turned out, jumped from between parked cars, appeared in front of Trevor's motorcycle and there was not enough time or distance to stop, or even slide to one side and avoid the man. The handlebar clipped the captain, sent him reeling and nearly caused Trevor to run into a car. But he was able to maintain control and stop. He called to the captain, "Sir, are you okay?"

"I'm better than okay," replied the captain grinning impishly. "One of our fly boys just dropped the big one on Japan. They've got no choice but to surrender." With that said he yelled loudly, "Hip-hip-hooray for America!" and continued up the street.

That was how Trevor learned the United States had dropped an atomic bomb on the Japanese city of Hiroshima. Later he listened to the radio broadcast as President Harry Truman spoke from the cruiser, *USS Augusta*, in the mid-Atlantic. The President said the atom bomb unleashed over

Hiroshima was 2,000 times more powerful than the largest bomb ever deployed, and he went on to say it was an American B-29 Super Fortress – the same type of airplane Trevor had been trained to crew – that delivered the fatal bomb. The President warned, "If Japan does not now accept our terms they may expect a rain of ruin from the air the like of which has never been seen on earth. Behind this air attack will follow by sea and land forces in such number and power as they have not yet seen, but with fighting skill of which they are already aware."

Trevor had conflicting emotions about this astounding event that had transpired a half-world away. He was grateful the war with Japan would soon be coming to an end, but he had heard the casualty report, that 100,000 Japanese civilians had been vaporized in the explosion at Hiroshima, and he thought about Tetsua and his other Japanese American classmates and wondered about their reaction to the bombing. Did any of them have family members who might have been killed or wounded in the blast? Trevor respected the fact not all Japanese were the enemy. He felt sorry for the carnage the war had caused to both countries, a war spawned by ruthless dictators and shrewd politicians.

Three days later a second atomic bomb was dropped on Nagasaki, Japan killing another 100,000 people. Six days later Japan surrendered. The war in the Pacific had ended.

*****

Trevor returned to Hood River for one final leave before being discharged from the Air Force. Once again his first stop was to see his fiancée, Betty. There was no doubt in Trevor's mind he was madly in love with Betty and now that his military obligation had all but been fulfilled he was looking forward to getting married and enrolling in college to become a teacher. Life was going to be good.

After spending the day together Trevor walked Betty home. She said she had to be at work early the following morning and needed her sleep. He kissed her goodnight at the door and told her she was beautiful. She made a little face, brushing the compliment away with a shake of her hand, went inside and closed the door. As Trevor walked down the steps he thought his Betty had been somehow different this time, distant maybe, but it was not something he dwelled on. Sometimes Betty could be a little moody like that. It was no big deal; not to Trevor it wasn't.

Trevor was walking along the street when Danny, a buddy he had gone to high school with, pulled alongside in his car, cranked down his window and called, "Hey, soldier, wanna lift?" He leaned across the seat and kicked open the door for Trevor.

Danny had an open bottle of beer propped between his legs and the remainder of the six-pack on the seat. He offered one to Trevor. "Don't mind if I do," said Trevor, pulling a bottle free and using a church key to flick off the cap.

"Home on leave?" asked Danny.

Trevor took a sip before answering. "Yup."

"When are they gonna discharge you?"

"It's in the works," responded Trevor.

"Still down in Texas?"

"Yup."

"Long way from home."

"Sure is," said Trevor.

"Not very talkative tonight," said Danny. "Somethin' botherin' you?"

"Nope."

"Been to see Betty?"

A stupid impulse struck Trevor. He blurted, "Betty and I broke up." Why he said such a crazy thing he never did know, never will know. But once those words were spoken they hung in the air with all the potential for mass destruction as the ugly gray mushroom cloud rising from the detonation of an A-bomb.

Danny turned and stared at Trevor. Perhaps he was trying to gauge whether this was true. Had Trevor and his high school sweetheart, the prettiest girl in the Hood River Valley, really broken up? Trevor stared straight ahead. He looked almost morose. A few seconds more and he would have burst into laugher and said of course they had not broken up; they were still engaged, as tight as ever, and would be married as soon as his discharge came through. He would invite Danny to the wedding.

Apparently Trevor played the part of the spurned lover all too well, or he played it a little too long. In that brittle pause between statement of fact and denial Danny made up his mind, returned his attention to the road, took a long pull from his beer and divulged, "Well, in that case I've got something to tell you, something that's been eating at my gut because I thought you needed to know. I didn't want to have to be the one to tell you this. But now since you and Betty aren't together any more...."

Trevor said nothing. The cold beer in his hand no longer felt cold. All Trevor could feel was a sinking sensation, the same as what a condemned man must suffer waiting for the gallows door to trip and the noose to come tight. He didn't have to wait long.

"Here a few weeks back Pete come home on leave from the Navy," said Danny. "You probably knew Pete and Betty went together back before you started going with her." Danny, pausing to let that information sink in, plunged ahead with a peculiar eagerness, as though he could hardly wait to deliver the hurtful news. And then again maybe he had had his eye on Betty all along and was just waiting for his opportunity.

"Anyway, I ran into Pete at the drugstore," said Danny. "He said he was there to buy another dozen condoms. See, Pete and Betty were shacked up in a motel. You know Pete's been all over the world, but he done told me Betty was the best piece he ever had. He said that, she was the best."

Those vicious words and all they conveyed struck Trevor like the cold steel of a double-edged sword plunged into his belly up to the hilt. The wind went out of him and he could not draw a breath. He was light-headed, dizzy, disoriented and a wave of nausea washed over him, yet he managed to groan, "Stop the car."

Trevor jerked at the handle, opened the door, and as the car came to a rolling stop he tumbled onto the ground, stumbled to his feet and lurched away. Danny called, "Hey buddy, thought you'd want to know." He leaned across the seat, pulled the door shut and dropped the Plymouth in gear.

Trevor did not want to know; especially did not want to believe his Betty could have been with another man. He and Betty were engaged. She was wearing his ring. How could she? Why would she?

Once the initial shock began to wear off Trevor knew he would have to confront Betty; knew she would cry and ask for his forgiveness. But in his mind forgiveness was not possible. He could never forgive and never forget. He knew that about himself. And he vowed he would never again open his heart and trust a woman. This hurt too much and when his legs were no longer able to hold his weight he wobbled and slowly sank onto his knees, and pitching forward he caught himself on his hands. He was violently sick in the dry, dead grass at the side of the road.

"His soft warble melts the ear, as the snow is melting in the valleys around."

– Henry David Thoreau

Vivian

~ Chapter Four ~

I did love Betty; still do. You don't quit loving someone because of something they did that hurt you. But after I learned what she had done – I never did blame Pete – I knew I could never trust her again. Really, for a time there I didn't want to trust or allow myself to love any woman except for my mother. I convinced myself if I was able to hunt and fish to my heart's content, go to college, get my certificate and start teaching, that would be enough and I'd be happy. The last thing I wanted was to get hung up on another woman. But then I met Viv and my life changed – I started to live again.

After being discharged from the Air Force Trevor returned to the Hood River Valley and found work driving truck in the harvest, hauling packed fruit across the river to the cold storage facility at Underwood, Washington. The trips were a continuous string of mindless miles, punctuated by orchards with pickers on wooden ladders and dryland fields of wheat where combines clattered, reels spun, wheat was sheared and golden grain poured into the bins. Trevor endured the repetition, the oppressive heat, and thought how terrible it was for love to die like wheat pinched off by a combine. Each pass the combine made the swath of sun-bright stubble grew wider and wider and beyond the fields stood the hazy image of Mount Hood. This sight gave Trevor a measure of comfort and reassurance; to know that no matter what devastation occurred in his world, the majestic mountain was always there.

Trevor enrolled for fall term at Oregon College of Education (OCE). He moved into a house on Clay Street with Rollie, an upperclassman who had interrupted his college to go in the service and had returned from overseas to finish his degree in secondary education. Rollie was tall and athletic. He lived and breathed sports and wanted to be a high school coach when he graduated. He kept himself in the peak of condition, didn't drink or smoke and was a guard on the OCE basketball team and a pitcher on the baseball team. He was a bit of a dandy when it came to dressing and preferred slacks and pressed shirts or knit sweaters. He was handsome in the mold of pretty boy actor Tyrone Power, and slicked back his hair with Brylcreem pomade the same way Tyrone did. Rollie had received a generous inheritance from a departed uncle and had spending money in his pocket and a burning desire to buy a new car. What he wanted was a 2-door Chevrolet cabriolet and had his eye on a gleaming white convertible with a top to match and maroon cloth seats. It graced the showroom floor of the Chevrolet dealership in Salem.

Rollie told Trevor about the car, saying it was "absolutely gorgeous," and that it was quick and responsive with a three-speed manual shift transmission and that it "runs as quiet as an electric sewing machine." He bragged the top went up and down powered by a motor and there was plenty of chrome and even a wood grain dash. He said there was no other car on the road like it and added, "When I drive around I'll have to beat the girls off with a stick."

Rollie bought the Chevrolet, and when he drove up to their house Trevor saw his friend had not exaggerated. The car was all he had said it was and more. And while Trevor was looking it over two college girls happened by and asked if they could go for a ride. Rollie gave Trevor a wink, said, "See," and told the girls and Trevor to hop in. But Trevor begged off, said he would catch a ride later, that he had to study. The real reason for his reluctance was his heart was still hurting from Betty. He was not interested in girls or trying to kindle a new romance.

Rollie wheeled the cabriolet, top down, onto the road, accelerated quickly and grabbed second gear. The two girls sitting up front with him laughed at the wonderful display of speed, shook out their hair and let the wind blow through the long strands. Trevor stood watching and thinking how unfair life could be. Rollie had it all; good looks, charm, spending money and now the new car. How could any girl in her right mind ever resist Rollie?

Each afternoon Rollie drove his car onto the lawn where he washed it. And on Saturday he waxed the body and chrome until it gleamed with his handsome reflection. Trevor did not own a car. He had sold his motorcycle in Texas, was paying for school on the GI bill and had to budget his money. If Rollie didn't happen to be going his way, Trevor walked.

*****

Morlan's Confectionary was the meeting place in Monmouth for locals as well as students from OCE. The store, located on the corner of Main and Monmouth streets, occupied the bottom floor of an imposing two-story red brick building. Tall windows allowed light to cascade through and onto a wide array of displays. The store, originally opened in the early 1900s by Amos Morlan, had sold college textbooks until Howard Morlan took over the business from his father before the war. Howard added to the bookstore bringing in candy, baking supplies, cake decorations, tobacco, cards and collectibles. A pair of pinball machines stood against one wall and professors and students played between classes, dropping in nickels to increase the odds, shooting silver balls, and if Lady Luck was with them, they won. In conservative Monmouth, gambling was on par with selling or consuming alcohol and strictly forbidden, forcing Howard to pay off under the table. But the real attraction at Morlan's was the soda fountain where soft drinks, malts, ice cream, coffee, hot chocolate and homemade lemonade were served. Howard, a short, plump, balding man, wore heavy-rimmed glasses and made lemonade from a syrupy concentrate. He claimed there was no better lemonade in the entire world. Howard performed the bulk of the work at Morlan's, but he was an astute businessman and employed a bevy of attractive young ladies to work part-time, waiting on customers who sat on the revolving stools at the counter or in the two booths that comprised the fountain section. People frequented Morlan's to shop for specific items, enjoy a treat from the fountain, or for no better reason than to see and be seen.

Trevor and Rollie were at Morlan's grabbing a soda one Saturday afternoon. They sat in a booth so they could be the first to see who came through the tall doors. Rollie was talking about sports, the upcoming basketball season and stating all the reasons the OCE Wolves should win the conference title. Perry Como was singing his new hit, *"Till the End of Time,"* on the jukebox.

Till the end of time, long as stars are in the blue
Long as there's a Spring of birds to sing I'll go on loving you

Two girls walked through the doors. Trevor recognized Helen. She was in his Introduction to Western Civilization class. But the other girl was the one who attracted his immediate attention. She was not the most beautiful or exotic young woman he had ever seen. She was wearing nothing special – boots, a gray wool skirt and a blue blouse with a little white lace near the neck. Her stride, although graceful and carefree, was not particularly sexy. And yet there was an intriguing quality about this new girl that totally captivated Trevor.

"Hi Trevor. Hi Rollie," called Helen gleefully.

"Hey there," said Trevor.

"Hey there," said Rollie.

When the new girl passed the booth she gave a sidelong glance and Trevor suddenly knew exactly what the attraction was, it was her eyes – soft, brown eyes that gave off a shower of blue-green sparks – and Trevor felt dizzy as he subconsciously became aware of Perry Como's soothing voice.

Till the end of time, long as roses bloom in May
My love for you will grow deeper with every passing day

When Trevor looked again the new girl was running her hands over her bottom to smooth her skirt and sliding up and on to one of the high stools. She was laughing at something Rollie had said. Trevor had missed it.

"Holy shit," said Rollie, mostly under his breath. "That girl is really something."

"Helen?" asked Trevor. He hoped it was Helen.

"Hell no," hissed Rollie, "that other girl."

Till the wells run dry and each mountain disappears
I'll be there for you to care for you through laughter and
    through tears

"I've gotta talk to her," said Rollie pushing himself up and out of the booth. "Come on," he directed. But he did not wait for Trevor. He strolled the short distance across the room and took up a commanding position between the girls. Trevor followed, but when he got there he wasn't able to find a comfortable spot to stand and hung back.

"How are you doing?" asked Helen.

"Fine," said Trevor.

With Helen and Trevor now occupied in conversation Rollie slid a half step closer to the new girl. Trevor didn't like the way this was going and blurted, "So who's your friend? Aren't you going to introduce us?"

So take my heart in sweet surrender and tenderly say that I'm
The one you love and live for till the end of time

"Forgive my bad manners," said Helen with a laugh. "Vivian, I would like you to meet Trevor Russell. Trevor, this is Vivian Richardson. She's going to school at the University of Oregon. Trevor is going to school here. We're in Western Civ. together. I guess you've already met Rollie."

"He just introduced himself," said Vivian. Her voice was friendly with a lyrical quality like her words were musical notes. She stuck out her hand and Trevor took it. Her touch excited him but it was the sparkle of her brown eyes rimmed with flecks of blue and green that awakened his passion.

Till the wells run dry and each mountain disappears
I'll be there for you to care for you through laughter and
    through tears

Trevor did not let go of Vivian's hand but used it as leverage to pull himself toward her. She was wearing very little makeup, just a touch of eye shadow and enough mascara to accent her stunning eyes. Trevor guessed if she was wearing perfume it would be light and smell sweet, but not overpoweringly sweet, maybe lavender. Hoop earrings dangled from her ear lobes. Her hair was stylishly cut. She seemed to occupy the middle ground, not too dressy and not too casual. But it was those eyes, those eyes. He finally released her hand and nodded in the direction of the jukebox, where colored lights flashed, and asked, "Do you like Perry Como?"

"Adore him," said Vivian. "His singing is so heartfelt, or it seems to be."

Before Trevor drew his next breath, and as crazy as it may sound, he was absolutely sure in that sliver of time that Vivian was the one, the one he was destined to spend his life with. And that thought, that she was the one, scared the hell out of Trevor. He had never been sure like that with Betty. He took one small, jolting step backward.

Rollie seized the opportunity to push his way between Trevor and Vivian. He asked Vivian, "Did you see that new white convertible parked out front?"

Vivian nodded, said it was a beautiful automobile and with more than a trace of skepticism added, "And I suppose you own it?"

"As a matter of fact I do," bragged Rollie. He took Vivian by the elbow and said, "Wanna go for a spin?"

Vivian looked past Trevor toward Helen for an answer.

"We have time," said Helen. "Sure."

"After we finish our Cokes," said Vivian.

*So take my heart in sweet surrender and tenderly say that I'm
The one you love and live for till the end of time*

*****

The four of them did go for a ride, but the seating arrangement was not how Rollie had it planned. He wanted to divide the girls, have Vivian sit beside him, but she crawled in back joining Helen, and Trevor sat up front. They drove north on Highway 99 West, cut over on a side road and followed the Willamette River to Independence. Returning to Monmouth Rollie dropped the girls off at Helen's car. He asked Vivian if he could have her phone number. She smiled her acceptance and Rollie asked, "When are you coming back here?"

"Next weekend," said Vivian.

"How about if we get together?" asked Rollie. "Maybe go see a movie."

Vivian was willing. "Okay," she said, handing Rollie the slip of paper with her phone number. "Give me a call mid-week."

Rollie turned to Trevor after Vivian and Helen had departed and said, "I'm gonna let you in on a little secret. That Vivian is definitely special. Next weekend when she and I go out on a date I'll find out exactly how special."

Rollie did call Vivian and it was decided she would come to Monmouth, to the house Rollie shared with Trevor, on Saturday at six o'clock. They talked about which movie they wanted to see. Vivian had her heart set on *"Blue Sky"* staring Bing Crosby and Fred Astaire, but Rollie said he didn't like singing and dancing and suggested *"The Postman Always Rings Twice"* staring Lana Turner and John Garfield. They could not seem to agree on which movie to see and decided to wait until Saturday to make their decision.

Trevor wrestled with his emotions. After all he had been wrong in trusting Betty and now he doubted what his instincts were telling him, that Vivian was the one he was destined to be with. Apparently Vivian wanted to be with Rollie. But that was understandable, what girl in her right mind wouldn't want to be with Rollie? It was Rollie who had stepped to the plate and asked Vivian out on a date, and now Trevor castigated himself for hanging back. Fate it seemed was almost always decided by the aggressor. And then Trevor didn't want to think about Vivian and Rollie's upcoming date any more. He picked up his fishing rod, walked to a little stream nearby and proceeded to drown a bucket of fat night crawlers.

*****

On Friday, Rollie met Frankie on the tennis court. She was a divorcee, no children, 10 years older than Rollie. She was trim and tan and although she didn't know much about tennis, she knew exactly how to play Rollie. She seduced him with praise, complimenting him on his athletic abilities and his sculpted body; she cajoled and flirted and before afternoon had turned to evening, Frankie had Rollie in her bed.

Rollie considered himself a playboy and thought he knew a thing or two about lovemaking, but Frankie taught him more. She taught him to be gentle, what words to whisper and she showed him the places on a woman's body that were the most sensitive; exactly where and how to touch and stroke those places. When morning dawned Frankie whispered in Rollie's ear she was kidnapping him. They would spend the day in Portland and the night making passionate love at a downtown hotel.

*****

On Saturday Trevor tried to study but lacked the ability to concentrate. He kept restlessly glancing at his watch, expecting at any moment to see Rollie's white Chevy turn off Clay Street and come gliding up the driveway. But it never happened. Rollie was with Frankie and failed to come home. A few minutes after six o'clock Vivian drove in and got out of her father's 1941 Ford. Trevor leaped to his feet at the sound of the car door slamming. He was wearing a shirt he had ironed earlier. His hair was freshly combed. He waited until Vivian had marched up the steps and knocked and then he opened the door.

Vivian stood on the landing; broken sunlight slanting through the leaves of tall trees fell around her in a lively mosaic of light and shadow. Vivian seemed surprised Rollie was not there to greet her. It showed in her expression. She hesitantly asked, "Is Rollie here?"

"No," responded Trevor, and then with more conviction and confidence than he felt he added, "But I am. Why don't you come in?" He stepped back and held open the door, directing Vivian to the couch. He said, "Have a seat." And then he asked, "What can I get you – Coke, ice water, tea?"

"Nothing," she said. Later she would change her mind. "Rollie...?"

"Don't concern yourself with him," responded Trevor. "He got called out of town and asked me to fill in and be your date. Hope you don't mind."

Vivian looked puzzled, but only for an instant. She recovered, smiled and coyly asked, "So, what do you want to do on our *date*?"

"I thought we could sit here and visit for a little while. I'd like to get to know you," said Trevor. "And then maybe we can catch a movie. I've heard good things about *"Blue Sky."*

"Perfect," said Vivian. "I've wanted to see that one."

They sat and talked about a lot of things; books and poetry, birds and animals, family stories, growing up stories and family histories. Vivian said she had been 11 years old when her mother died. She said her father, Earle Richardson, was the owner/publisher of the *Polk County Itemizer-Observer*, the weekly newspaper in the nearby town of Dallas, and that he expected her to come home and take over the newspaper after she had completed her degree in journalism at the University of Oregon. They talked about fishing. Vivian said she loved to fish. They discussed rivers and streams, beavers and mule deer, blue herons and geese, and how much they both enjoyed writers who could put into words what they felt in their soul. They talked about nature, isolation and solitude. That first evening together they talked so much they missed the show. When they realized what they had done they laughed about it. Trevor suggested they catch the Sunday matinee. Vivian said that sounded like fun.

*****

Rollie came dragging in Sunday evening long after Vivian had left and returned to Eugene and the University of Oregon. He threw himself onto the couch, saying. "God, what a weekend!"

"You had fun?" asked Trevor.

"What can I say," said Rollie. "It was wild."

"You missed your date with Vivian."

"Ah shit," said Rollie hitting the heel of his right hand against his forehead. "She'll forgive me."

"I took her out."

"Did she say when she's coming back?" asked Rollie, ignoring Trevor's comment.

"Weekend after next," said Trevor. "We have a date to go fishing. We really hit it off. I like her."

Rollie sat up straight. "You doggin' my girl?"

"She's not your girl," said Trevor defensively. In that moment he would have fought for Vivian. Maybe Rollie could read the stern conviction in his roommate because he lay back down, stretched and groaned.

"You want her, take her. I got my hands full with Frankie. That woman is way more than any one man can handle."

*****

Trevor and Vivian did go fishing. They sat under a majestic oak tree on the bank of a small stream that tumbled from high in the Coast Range toward the floor of the Willamette Valley. They watched their red and white fishing bobbers intently and each time one dipped below the flat sheen of the water they took turns reeling in the fish. Afternoon sunlight filtered through the leaves and shadows constantly shifted and changed. The sun went down and the faint glow of stars began to dot the steely grayness of the sky. Finally, reluctantly it seemed, they went back to Trevor's house to cook the fish they had caught. That night when Vivian went to leave, Trevor kissed her for the first time.

On the drive home Vivian relived the wonderful day she had spent with Trevor. It had been so relaxing and Trevor was such fun to be with. She recalled the details of his face, down to the slight scar above his left eye – from a head butt in a boxing match he said – and she even remembered the individual calluses on his hands that proved he was a hard worker. She liked that he had served his country during a time of war and she recognized him as being a young man with principals and strong convictions about right and wrong. But most of all Vivian liked the sound of Trevor's voice. He spoke with a slight drawl from having grown up east of the mountains. It was an almost folksy accent, not really an accent she guessed, but more a twang. She remembered the sounds when she had closed her eyes and listened to his voice and the soft gurgle of the stream as it flowed and tumbled over mossy rocks and into the pool where they were fishing. In that moment she had found peace and contentment.

And as she neared the city limits of Eugene, Vivian was startled by her intimate thoughts about Trevor Russell. She already had a boyfriend, a handsome fraternity boy majoring in political science. He came from a wealthy Portland family and held lofty dreams of running for political office. He was a catch, no doubt about it. And he had professed his love for Vivian. On the other hand Trevor was just such a genuinely nice guy. What was a girl to do?

*****

Two months passed before Trevor saw Vivian again. That meeting was born of tragedy. Vivian's grandfather had passed away. She came home for the funeral and called Trevor to tell him the disconcerting news. He asked if he could see her. She agreed, but on the drive to Monmouth the confusion building inside her became a furious boil of emotions. And then when she got to the house Trevor was so anxious to be with her that he rushed to open the car door before she had even turned off the engine. He barely gave her room to exit and then quickly gathered her in his arms, thanking her for coming and saying how good it was to see her. And she felt, tucked into the cradle of his embrace, both small and sheltered and dare she even think it, but she felt *loved*. It seemed so natural to her, as if this one moment was what she had wanted and been waiting for all her life.

"Good to see you, too," she found herself saying.

"I missed you," he whispered in immediate response.

The voice, Trevor's voice, brought Vivian around and made her realize she was feeling something she had not intended to feel. After all, two months had passed since she had seen him last and a lot had happened.

That day they had spent together fishing, a glorious day to be sure, was just one day. And when it was over Vivian had returned to Eugene. And now she was trying to convince herself that what she had done had been the right thing.

Vivian's boyfriend had proposed to her. She said yes. They were engaged to be married. And now she was wearing his ring; a gold band featuring dazzling diamonds and three majestic heart-shaped peridot gemstones – Vivian's birthstone. Her future was set, or so it seemed, and after graduating from college the couple would move home to Dallas and take over the newspaper. Vivian's husband would use the newspaper as a springboard into politics and she saw herself on the arm of a governor, or maybe a state senator. She had thought that was what she wanted. She thought she loved him. And now with Trevor's arms holding her tightly she was acutely aware of the ring. She hoped Trevor did not notice it.

"I'm so sorry," said Trevor. His words were sincere and heartfelt.

Vivian broke off the embrace. Her brow was knit in bewilderment as to why Trevor would be sorry. She was the one who should be saying those words; sorry for pushing his memory away, sorry for pushing him away, sorry for denying she had feelings for him and sorry for saying yes to another man.

"Your grandfather," explained Trevor. "I'm sorry for your loss."

With a wild sense of relief Vivian's eyes suddenly brimmed with tears. Trevor tenderly wiped those tears away from the corners of her eyes with his thumbs. He asked if she was okay and she nodded, sniffled and said she didn't mean to cry. He said it was okay, that she needed to be able to express her grief. He never suspected the truth; the tears were meant for him and the pain she would cause him when she told him she was going to be married. Not a single one of those tears was for Vivian's grandfather.

Vivian gave a nervous little laugh and tried to compose herself. She sniffled once more. "Thanks for your concern," she said, and her eyes darted about as unsettled as a nighthawk in flight. When her gaze landed on Trevor it lingered there and she felt tears building once more. To keep them from breaching she asked, "Could I please have a glass of water?"

"Oh sure," said Trevor and he led her toward the house. While climbing the stairs Vivian slipped off the gaudy engagement ring and tucked it in her pocket.

*****

It was well into evening but still Vivian could not bring herself to leave, not quite yet. Standing near Trevor on the front porch, running her hands through her hair, Vivian took a deep breath and held it for a moment enjoying the earthy aromas of late autumn. As she exhaled the wind sprang to life, pulling loose yellow leaves that fell gently and were pushed along on the ground. She liked that too. Wind fanned her warm cheeks. Trevor pulled her to him then and she felt the tension in her shoulders and neck begin to dissipate. The wind sighed. The sky darkened. A soft rain fell.

The words – telling Trevor she was engaged to be married – formed in Vivian's mind, but she could not speak them. At one point she thought she could, but Trevor kissed her and she felt the warmth of his lips against her lips and knew all too well. She closed her eyes and faded into that kiss. And when they parted there was no need to tell him anything. Vivian knew what she must do if she was to follow her heart.

*****

Trevor stood and watched her drive away. He was powerless to stop her. And as the red glow of the car's taillights rounded the corner and disappeared he wanted to shout, "Vivian, I love you." The wind came up moaning through the bare branches and the rain came down with a hard, driving urgency.

*****

The following weekend Vivian came home once more. Earle Richardson, Vivian's father, was surprised to see her. It was sweet she would visit two weekends in a row and he thought maybe she was worried about him and how he was adjusting to the death of his father. But he soon learned the real reason when Vivian asked to borrow the car.

"Where are you going?" he wanted to know. She said to meet a friend. He pressed for more information. She said to see a young man.

"But I thought you had a fellow," said Earle. "Aren't you engaged?"

Vivian sighed, "I broke it off."

"But you said he was a nice guy. You said he treated you well." Earle seemed confused by this turn of events. But there was more to it than that. He was tired of bringing out a weekly newspaper: selling ads, writing copy, the production work and then delivering the damn things. He wanted to retire and have his daughter take over. And now that was not going to happen.

"He was a nice guy, is a nice guy," said Vivian correcting herself. She was feeling guilty and didn't know how she was supposed to respond to her father. "We had fun together. He's smart and good looking and would be a wonderful husband. He loves me. I love him, too."

"Think the two of you will get back together?" asked Earle, grasping at possibilities.

"No."

"Why?" asked Earle, trying hard to understand.

"There was something missing. I don't know," said Vivian. "A *spark*. I didn't feel a *spark*."

"And this new fellow, he gives you a *spark*?" In that instant Earle made up his mind he would never like this new fellow in Vivian's life, the one who had caused the split between her and her fiancé and ruined all his plans to retire from the newspaper business and take life easy for a few years before he kicked the bucket.

"Oh, Daddy, I don't know," said Vivian. She smiled weakly, shrugged and shook her head. "Maybe I'm just not ready to be married."

Earle handed over the keys. Vivian took them, gave her father a peck on his cheek, and threw a quick thank you in his direction as she hurried out the door, thankful to be done with the inquisition and on her way to see Trevor. She hoped she was doing the right thing. The right thing: was Trevor the right thing? She didn't know. But he made her feel differently than anyone ever had, including her fiancé, her *ex-fiancé*. Could she explain it? No. And that irritated her the most because she was a writer and should be able to use words to describe anything and everything. Out of annoyance she muttered, "Damn it."

*****

Vivian reached Trevor's house and found him dressed in his usual attire – blue jeans, flannel shirt, work boots – and in the process of fixing himself a bite to eat. He asked if she would like to join him. She said sure and trying to be helpful, volunteered, "Want me to set the table?"

"Okay," said Trevor. He was cutting bread with a knife and used the knife as a pointer. "You'll find spoons in that drawer." He stopped what he was doing to look at her. He said, "Have I ever mentioned you have fantastic eyes?"

Vivian batted her brown eyelashes at him. She was happy with the compliment. She liked it that Trevor made her feel like a woman.

Trevor stepped into the pantry and grabbed two cans of Campbell's Vegetable Soup. He blew dust off the lids, set the cans on the counter and opened them with a crank can opener. He set the lids aside and used the sharp knife to slice butter off the cube and spread it on the bread. He took the bread and placed a slice on the open top of each soup can. He carried these to the dining room table where Vivian had carefully placed two plates with bowls on top and a knife, fork and spoon neatly arranged beside a white napkin.

"Where did you find the napkins?" asked Trevor.

"In the back of the utensil drawer," said Vivian with a smile, but that smile quickly faded when Trevor plunked a can of soup down on her bowl, the bread on top like a big, floppy hat. She reached and touched the can. It was cold.

"You're not going to warm it?" she asked incredulously.

"Never do," said Trevor. He was already spooning the cold soup into his mouth. He tore off a hunk of bread with his teeth and chewed that too.

"And this is what you eat and how you eat it?"

"Yup," said Trevor. "This way I don't have dirty dishes, and from a nutritional standpoint it gives me all the vitamins my body needs, from vegetables to meat. Only costs 15 cents a can. Some days I eat three or four cans."

In spite of what Vivian concluded were his dubious manners and questionable reasoning, she forced herself to laugh. "Mister, allow me to let you in on a little secret. You are in desperate need of a good woman who will soften some of your rough edges."

"You want to apply for the job?"

"I just might," said Vivian with a wicked grin.

"Have I ever told you, you have beautiful eyes?"

"You mentioned that fact in passing. Thank you. But compliments only get you so far. Now, is there any chance you could find it in your heart to get up, put my soup in a pan, warm it and pour the contents in this bowl just to prove you know what civilization is all about."

And when Trevor brought the soup back to the table he already had it in a bowl. A towel was neatly folded over one forearm and he replaced the bowl on Vivian's plate with the flair of a waiter at an uptown restaurant. But unlike a waiter he bent and kissed Vivian's neck. Quickly regaining his professional demeanor he stood at rigid attention. "Does madam require anything more?"

She joked back. "Nothing more at this time, thank you."

Trevor watched her scoop a dainty spoonful of soup and blow wrinkles across the surface to cool it. He wondered if she ever dreamed of lying naked with him. Did they ever make love in her dreams? He had had those dreams nearly every night since he first met her. Some nights he woke up with a physical ache for her. His need was that great.

By Trevor's silence Vivian sensed he was probably thinking about her, although she didn't know specifically what he might be thinking. If she had known the true extent of his thoughts she would have blushed with embarrassment.

Later they went for a walk. The clouds were thick, low and gray, pregnant with moisture. Although rain threatened it had not yet arrived. Beneath their feet fallen leaves crunched. They held hands and watched gray squirrels with long, bushy tails scurry about, bouncing from limb to limb, searching for food to store for winter. When Vivian let go of his hand and wrapped her arms around herself to ward off the chill, Trevor took notice, stripped off his jacket and slung it over her shoulders poncho style.

"Oh, no," she started to protest but Trevor insisted she keep the jacket. For a long time they walked in near silence, each sifting through their personal thoughts. Trevor appreciated the silence she allowed him. He was never one to fill up every moment with useless chatter.

Vivian was busy contemplating why Trevor was the one person who was capable of invoking certain feelings in her that no other man ever had. She had first become aware of those emotions the day they went fishing. Sitting on the ground beside Trevor she had felt stirrings that were like tiny specks of gold swirling through black sand and it was not until a fine layer had built up that she was forced to acknowledge their existence. And now she had to face the fact, she was falling in love with Trevor Russell.

Trevor was the one who finally broke the silence. "Why are you smiling?"

"Was I?" asked Vivian.

"Yes you certainly were. Why?"

"Just thinking."

"What about?" Trevor had an idea what it was about, but he wanted her to say it, say she was in love with him.

"Private thoughts," she countered. Silence prevailed.

But Trevor wasn't about to give up. He toyed with her. "You said you could share anything with me." He pouted, sticking out his lower lip in mock exaggeration. He bent at the waist to purposely look into her beautiful brown eyes flecked with the blue of the sky and the green of Hood River in summer. The eyes gave her away.

The temperature continued to drop a few more degrees. Errant drops of rain splattered the sidewalk in front of them, and knowing a deluge would soon follow, Vivian said, "We best get back." They quickened their pace. A dog barked. Somewhere in the distance a woodpecker could be heard hammering a tree. The rain picked up. Vivian ran a hand through her hair, feeling its wetness. She pulled Trevor's jacket even closer around her shoulders, holding it closed. And even though his shirt and pants were already drenched Trevor started running, coaxing Vivian to run with him, claiming, "We've gotta hurry. I don't wanna get wet." They ran and the gray sky flashed and a moment later thunder boomed. They reached the porch. There was more lightning, more thunder.

Vivian shouted to be heard over the noise of the storm, "I don't want us to ever lose our playfulness."

"We won't," Trevor assured her. They kissed. Lightning lit the blue-black sky and rain roared down against the roof.

*****

Fall turned to winter and winter reluctantly became spring. Vivian came home as often as she could. Her romance with Trevor flourished like wildflowers that, with a little rain and sunshine, are thrust upward from the fertile soil of the Willamette Valley to blossom in a profusion of lively colors. When spring term ended Vivian moved home to Dallas where she devoted herself to helping her father at the newspaper. Nearly every evening she drove to Trevor's house on Clay Street in Monmouth so they could spend time together. Trevor had told her he loved her. She was sure he did. She felt the same way.

*****

Trevor and Vivian were sitting together in rocking chairs on the front porch of the house. The air was warm and close with humidity. A few clouds, having rolled in off the Pacific, were turning silver with the reflection of the moon and stood unmoving in the still night sky. Trevor kept a steady rhythm, rocking back and forth, the old chair squeaking at the same point every time. It was a reassuring sound, hypnotic almost.

Trevor was enrolled at OCE for the summer terms, planning to pick up nine hours the first session and signing up for another nine the second session. He still shared the house with Rollie but hardly ever saw his roommate. Rollie and Frankie were spending most of their time at her place.

As he rocked Trevor was thinking about love and how being with Vivian on a night like this filled him with a comforting warmth. In the distance crickets were chirping and frogs were adding to the musical cavalcade. Natural sounds were what he enjoyed most. He supposed this was the way life was meant to be lived; simple, pure and carefree. He never understood people who thought in terms of dollars and cents and accumulating assets and worldly goods. The best things in life were not for sale. Just then a car with only one headlight passed the house and when it slowed to turn a corner it backfired loudly.

"I have something to show you," said Vivian, reaching into her handbag sitting beside her rocker and withdrawing a paper. She handed it to Trevor. Enough light was leaking through from the front window that Trevor could see Vivian had signed up for the upcoming term at OCE. Her declared major was elementary education. He turned and looked at her questioningly.

She gave a nervous little laugh. "I thought if you were going to be involved in education, I should be too."

Nothing more was said, not for a long moment, and then Trevor began to whistle the lyrical Harry James tune, *"It's Been A Long, Long Time."* He switched to humming softly and then to tenderly sing the words, *"Kiss me once, then kiss me twice, then kiss me once again. It's been a long, long time. Haven't felt like this, my dear since I can't remember when. It's been a long, long time."* And then he did kiss her. He told her he loved her and his acknowledgement filled Vivian with joy.

Vivian having signed up for the summer school at OCE spoke volumes to Trevor. In his estimation it was proof positive she loved him, and was willing to give up her ambitions of a career in journalism to follow his lead. She was saying she wanted to share her life with him. And in that moment Trevor was so overcome with an awareness of his love for Vivian that he very nearly dropped to one knee in front of her and proposed on the spot. But his more practical side won out over his romanticism. He told himself they needed to wait. The GI Bill was providing barely enough income for him to go to school, nothing more, and he could certainly not support a wife. If they did get married one of them would have to drop out of school and find a job. That was not an acceptable option. Not to Trevor it wasn't. And so he was content to sit with Vivian and hold her hand. The muscles in his neck and shoulders began to let go of tension and he allowed his mind to wander to the days ahead when they would have children together.

Haven't felt like this my dear, since I can't remember when. It's been a long, long time. Kiss me once, then kiss me twice, then kiss me once again. ...

*****

The unusual thing about the baseball field on the OCE campus, unlike any other ball field in America, was the big leaf maple tree that grew just inside the fence and dominated far center field. The tree was several hundred years old, dating back to well before the arrival of the first white man, and the administration refused to even consider allowing for its removal. A special rule was instituted because of that tree. If a ball was hit into the tree and fell into the field of play, it was automatically treated as a ground field double. But only on rare occasions were balls ever hit far enough to touch the spreading branches of the stately tree.

One of Trevor's closest friends was Claude; a baseball player who was said to have major league talent and major league aspirations. It was Claude's dream to one day play for the New York Giants.

During an OCE playoff game Claude got a pair of towering hits that appeared to go above the highest reaches of the big leaf maple. But in both instances the ball hit a cluster of leaves, lost its forward momentum and fell inside the fence. In any other ballpark the hits would have been home runs, easily, but at OCE they were treated as ground field doubles. The last hit, coming in the bottom of the ninth, would have won the game for OCE but all Claude received for his effort was the opportunity to trot to second base and wait, hoping the next batter would drive him in. But that didn't happen. OCE lost and after the game Claude quietly vowed to get rid of that offending tree.

Claude knew Trevor had grown up in rural Hood River County and had had experience felling trees. He paid Trevor a visit. "I don't ever wanna get robbed and lose another game, never again. I've laid my hands on a couple of double-bit axes and a 12 foot cross-cut saw. I need your help 'cause tonight we're gonna cut down that goddamn maple tree."

It was near midnight and the moon was out and shining brightly when Claude and Trevor carried the lumberjacking tools onto the baseball field. They marched to the base of the big leaf maple and went to work. With quick, efficient strokes they employed the two-man cross-cut saw to make a deep cut on the face. Using the sharp double-bit axes they carved out the undercut and without hesitation moved to the backside of the enormous tree and started a cut slightly above the undercut. When the cross-cut blade dragged in the pitch, Claude squirted a little kerosene on the flat steel blade and they kept sawing. At last the tree gave a shudder and started on an arc, picking up speed until it crashed onto the ground with a thunderous racket.

"Let's get out of here," gasped Claude. He and Trevor grabbed their tools and ran away.

The following day maintenance workers began cutting the fallen tree into rounds for firewood. And although there was talk about identifying the guilty party or parties who were responsible for the vandalism – and Claude's name came up on the top of nearly everyone's list – the deed was done and very little effort was made to investigate the matter. The wood was hauled away and the only reminder the tree had ever stood in far center field was the gigantic stump trimmed to ground level.

*****

It was the dead of night and Trevor and Vivian were sitting on the grass near the stump of the fallen big leaf maple. Trevor had chosen this spot because it was a private place with some interesting personal history; he knew nobody would come onto the ball field in the dark. He told Vivian the story about when he and Claude had cut down the tree and she thought it was sad in a way, killing the tree, but it was funny, too. She leaned into Trevor and he responded by draping an arm around her shoulders and pulling her to him. She felt the heat of their mutual desire begin to build.

They had talked about this, the moment when they would come together and make love, and now the moment was upon them. Vivian thought it felt so right and so incredibly real. She lifted her head off Trevor's shoulder and looked at him, seeing his pale skin in the ambient starlight, using her fingertips to trace along his cheeks, nose and eyelids like a blind person affixing a face to memory. When he kissed her she closed her eyes and parted her lips. He ran a hand down her spine, fingers reaching, probing, touching. She lay back on the grass and began unbuttoning his shirt. Trevor felt the sensations of her nimble fingers touching his skin and sliding through the hair on his chest. He trembled with anticipation. They kissed with passion and desire and Trevor felt the pounding of Vivian's heart.

"Do you have it?" she whispered with a throaty urgency.

"Of course," Trevor responded. "It's in my wallet."

"You best get it out," whispered Vivian.

*****

Earle Richardson, Vivian's father, owned a fishing cabin on the south bank of the Siletz River. The road ran on the north side and the only way to reach the isolated cabin was by boat.

When the steelhead run was on the cabin was the perfect place to hole up, with miles of good water to fish and very few other fishermen.

A late summer run was in the river and Vivian and Trevor, along with Trevor's brother Gordon and his wife Jean, spent a weekend at the cabin. They thought, in addition to getting in some fishing, this would be the perfect opportunity, in a relaxed setting, for Vivian to get to know Gordon and Jean. They arrived at the cabin on Friday too late to fish, so they fixed a bite to eat, drank beer and sat around visiting. The following morning Trevor and Gordon were up early fishing; bouncing bright spinners down a long riffle and into a green pool. Gordon told his brother, "You got yourself a great gal there; what the hell you waiting for?"

"Don't know," shrugged Trevor.

"Best not let her get away," advised Gordon.

"We've talked," countered Trevor. "But with school and all...."

"Excuses. Excuses," said Gordon. "That one's a keeper."

Trevor told Vivian about his conversation with Gordon. Vivian asked Trevor how he had responded. Trevor replied, "I told him you and I'd get married one of these days, when we could afford it."

"If that's a proposal, I accept," shrieked Vivian, and she raised her voice even more and shouted to Gordon in the other room, "Your brother just asked me to marry him and I accepted."

Gordon and Jean rushed into the room. They hugged Vivian and welcomed her to the family. Trevor sat on the edge of the bed. He was dumbfounded and wondered if Vivian and Gordon had worked out this scenario in advance. But if they were in cahoots there wasn't a damn thing he could do about it. The strange thing was, if he had been able to put a stop to this, he might not want to. He smiled weakly.

"Well brother, I'm certainly glad you did the right thing and ask her to marry you," exclaimed Gordon.

"I did?" questioned Trevor.

Vivian hurried to him, sat on his lap, cooed in his ear, "You did and I accept." She gave him an exaggerated kiss, as if that was the clincher that sealed the deal. And then she told him, "I love you, Trevor." And finally Trevor did laugh.

*****

Between summer and fall terms Trevor returned to Odell and worked a double shift, eight hours moving apples and pears into cold storage and then as many hours as he could stay awake building wooden shipping crates. He was paid a penny apiece for the crates, and once he got in a routine he could build a crate a minute.

One weekend Vivian came for a visit and Trevor surprised her by slipping an engagement ring on her finger. And then he shocked her even more by saying, "Why are we putting off the inevitable, let's just get married."

Vivian wasn't sure. "Dad always wanted me to be married in the church. He wanted me to have this big wedding and a cake and...."

"What do you want?" asked Trevor.

"I want you. I want to be your wife. I want you to be my husband," said Vivian.

"Then let's do it. Let's elope," said Trevor enthusiastically.

They drove across the river to White Salmon, Washington, but at the courthouse they were told the Justice of the Peace was gone deer hunting and the clerk suggested they might try Goldendale. Trevor glanced at his watch. It was 3:30 p.m.

and Goldendale was better than 50 miles away. He grabbed Vivian by the hand and they rushed to the Ford sedan Vivian had borrowed from her father. With tires spinning and gravel pinging off the underside of the Ford they were off to get married.

Arriving at Goldendale with only minutes to spare before the courthouse closed, the clerk on duty informed Trevor and Vivian, "You need two witnesses to get married."

There were only two other people in the room, a couple waiting to get married. The fellow spoke up and asked Trevor, "Are you related to Gordon Russell?"

"Yeah, he's my brother," said Trevor.

"I went to school with Gordon. He was a grade ahead of me," said the groom to be.

An inspiration hit Trevor, "Will the two of you be our witnesses?"

"Sure, we'll stick around after we get married and do that for you," said the fellow.

Trevor turned to the clerk and triumphantly announced, "We have our witnesses. Now can we get married?"

"Ten dollars," said the clerk popping her gum. "Sign here."

The Justice of the Peace moved quickly through the simple ceremony. The "I dos" were said, papers were signed and a few minutes after 5 p.m. on September 6, 1946, Trevor and Vivian Russell became husband and wife. They honeymooned at a motel in The Dalles and their wedding supper consisted of a six pack of beer and cheese and crackers. The couple was deliciously happy.

The following day Vivian returned home and Trevor went back to work at the cold storage facility. Nobody was told about the elopement. That news would be kept a secret until Earle, Vivian's father, could be told at the right time and in the right way. But no matter what was said, and when it was said, he wasn't going to take it well. Vivian and Trevor were sure of that.

*****

Three weeks passed before Trevor could get any time off to travel to Dallas and visit his bride. During this time Mildred, Trevor's mother, became suspicious and confronted her son. Mildred always claimed she had psychic powers. She could predict when it would rain, the date of the first snowfall and name the person who would be the next visitor to come up the driveway. "You got something on your mind, don't you, son?"

Trevor denied it.

"What is it?"

"Nothing. I've got nothing on my mind."

"Yes you do," said Mildred. "It has something to do with that girl, with Vivian, and you are going to tell me."

"What makes you think that?" countered Trevor.

"The way you mope around," said Mildred. She was looking at him, through him it seemed and the answer suddenly came to her as bright as if a light bulb had been switched on. In an excited whisper she exclaimed, "The two of you ran off and got married, didn't you?"

Trevor's first inclination was to deny it, but he couldn't lie to his mother. He tried a slightly different tack, making her a part of the secret. He said, "If I tell you, you can't say anything to anybody. You have to promise."

"I knew it," said Mildred clapping her hands together in glee. "But why keep it a secret? You should shout out such wonderful news from the mountain top."

"Because," said Trevor, lowering his voice, "we don't want Vivian's father to get wind of it. See, Vivian is an only child and her dad had this big idea of her getting married in the church with all the bells and whistles. He wanted to walk up the aisle with his daughter and give her away. He had it all planned, down to the dress Vivian would wear and the flowers and all that. That's one reason. The second is that as long as she stays in school he puts a hundred bucks in her bank account every month. Without that Vivian couldn't afford to go to school."

*****

After work on Friday Trevor hitchhiked the 150 miles to Dallas. The sun was already down by the time he walked to the house Vivian shared with her father. Earle had told Trevor he was welcome to stay over whenever he was in town, and made a point of showing him the upstairs bedroom where he was to sleep. It went without saying that Vivian's bedroom, adjacent to the kitchen, was off limits, strictly off limits. Trevor always respected Earle's wishes.

But now they were married. This was different; anyway in Trevor's mind it was. After having a bite to eat the couple retired to Vivian's bedroom. They knew Earle would be working late at the newspaper office and thought they had time for intimacy before Trevor retired to the upstairs bedroom. When Earle did come home he would never be the wiser. That's what they thought. The plan was that on Saturday Earle would be sitting in his easy chair and they would tell him their big news. Vivian had practiced what she would say. She would start by telling her father how much she loved him. Then she would explain she loved Trevor and they had not been able to wait any longer and had impulsively gotten married. Earle would be disappointed, at first he would be, but Vivian was sure her father would come around and accept the fact, and accept Trevor as his son-in-law.

What happened was much different than what was planned. After making love Trevor and Vivian fell asleep. They did not hear Earle when he came in a little before midnight; did not hear him when he got up during the night to go to the bathroom. They awoke to Indian summer sunlight streaming in the east facing window. Out in the kitchen there was a clattering of pots and pans and the rich aroma of freshly perked coffee riding on the air.

"Jesus, Mary and Joseph," groaned Trevor quietly as he brought both hands to his head in a pretentious display of anguish.

Vivian's reaction was to tuck the sheet tightly around her naked body and not move, not make a sound.

"We're in quite a pickle here," whispered Trevor. Vivian remained silent. The look on her face was that of fear. In the other room bacon could now be heard sizzling in a fry pan on the stove and its unmistakable smell soon joined the aroma of the coffee. Two plates were set on the table followed a moment later by the tinny sounds of utensils joining the plates. Earle whistled the first stanza of *"Camp Town Races"* and broke it off to call, "Honey, better get up, breakfast is almost ready."

"Get dressed," instructed Vivian as she leaped from bed and began pulling on her clothes. She ran a brush through her hair and smacked her lips to bring out a little color without bothering to take the time to put on lipstick.

Trevor threw on his shirt, pulled up his pants, buckled his belt and slipped his feet into his boots. He leaned close to Vivian and asked, "What me to go out the window?"

"No," said Vivian. She opened a dresser drawer, removed the marriage license and took Trevor by the hand. He was still trying to tuck in the tail of his shirt when she opened the door and pulled him into the kitchen. Earle, who was holding the spatula and sliding the last egg in the fry pan onto a plate, stopped abruptly. He stared at them with wide-eyed surprise and disbelief. His eyebrows arched upward. His mouth flopped open.

"Daddy," said Vivian. She seemed very much in command, but Trevor could feel her damp hand shaking with nervousness. She went on, "Trevor and I are married." She held up the marriage license as if it was a war shield.

For a moment Earle said nothing, and when he did speak he did not try to mask his displeasure. He scowled. "I kinda guessed something like this might happen." He set the empty pan back on the stove, grabbed his coat and headed for the door, throwing over his shoulder, "I've got work to do at the office. Help yourselves to breakfast." And then he was gone. The thunder of the door slamming echoed off the walls.

Vivian turned to Trevor. "That went rather well, don't you think?"

Trevor didn't know if Vivian was going to laugh or cry. She was somewhere between the two extremes. Instead she took her normal seat at the table and motioned for Trevor to sit where her father usually sat. She said, "Better eat before it gets cold." And Trevor sat down and began eating.

*****

Now that they were married Trevor and Vivian qualified for subsidized student housing. They moved into a three bedroom apartment near the OCE campus. Earle, trying to help the couple living on such a tight budget, employed Trevor at a number of part-time newspaper jobs. Trevor laid out ads, set type, ran the folder and was even trained as a pressman. But he was slow arranging the lead type, was not quick enough on the folder and about the fourth time he failed to throw the proper lever and ink ran all over the press, Earle threw up his hands and informed Trevor, "You're not cut out for the newspaper business. You're just not coordinated enough."

Trevor's feelings were hurt. He wanted to say he was coordinated enough to hunt and fish, to play baseball and even to win the Golden Gloves boxing competition, but he didn't say any of that. Instead he took his firing in stride, went home and told Vivian, "I don't think your dad likes me."

"He will when he gets to know you," Vivian assured him. "Give him time."

*****

Rollie, Trevor's former roommate, was in trouble at school. His playboy ways had caught up to him. After being put on probation for having a grade point average of less than a two point, he was expelled from OCE.

When Trevor heard the news he asked his friend, "What are you going to do?"

"What can I do? Get a job I guess." Rollie seemed resigned to his fate.

"But you're a smart guy," said Trevor. "You just never learned to apply yourself. If you had ever studied you wouldn't be in this predicament."

"I know," said Rollie.

"Let me see what I can do. Maybe I can get you back in school," said Trevor.

"How are your gonna do that?"

"Talk to someone."

"Have at it," said Rollie. He wasn't going to hold out any false hope. He knew when his money ran out he'd have to find employment.

Trevor talked the matter over with Vivian. They both agreed that Rollie was worth saving. If he finished school he had the potential to become a great coach because his passion had always been sports. If he didn't get his degree there was no telling what would happen to him. Most likely he would squander his life drifting from one menial job to the next, and if he did that both Trevor and Vivian thought it would be a terrible waste of his talents. It was Vivian who suggested they rent Rollie a room, reasoning that if Rollie shared the cost of the apartment it would help their budget and in return Rollie, if he agreed to the terms, would have structure in his life and a rigid study schedule. All this was contingent on whether Trevor could get his friend another chance at school.

Trevor visited the school health nurse and talked her into examining Rollie's physical condition. She determined Rollie was slightly anemic and wrote a letter on his behalf, stating if he ate well-balanced, nutritional meals his mental performance would improve. Armed with that letter Trevor made an appointment to talk to the Dean of Students. He appealed to the dean, showed him the letter from the nurse and said if Rollie lived with him and Vivian he would have healthy meals and a strict study schedule. He went on to say Rollie was a good guy and predicted if given the chance he could become a productive member of society. The dean agreed. He directed Rollie to live at Trevor and Vivian's apartment and abide by their rules. He gave Rollie one term to prove himself.

That term Rollie sat down to a home cooked dinner every night. Sometimes his girlfriend, Pat, would join him. After dinner she returned to the dorm. Rollie was allowed one night out on the weekend and the rest of the time he spent studying. At the end of the term he was awarded all As and Bs. He married Pat and they moved into an apartment near

Trevor and Vivian. He graduated in secondary education and took a job in a school district near Portland where he taught and coached basketball.

*****

Trevor, after graduating from OCE, took a job as the superintendent, principal and coach at Springdale, a three teacher country school near Corbett, Oregon. Vivian was employed as a third grade teacher at nearby Rockdale Elementary. Three years later they moved to Oakridge, where Trevor became principal at Willamette City Elementary and Vivian taught kindergarten at Oakridge Elementary. They would remain in Oakridge for more than 30 years.

"I wish you bluebirds in the spring, To give your heart a song to sing, And then a kiss, But more than this, I wish you love!"

– *I Wish You Love*, **written by A. A. Beach & C. Trenet and recorded by Frank Sinatra, 1964**

The Perfect Family

~ Chapter Five ~

> *Vivian was an only child. She thought she had missed out on something by not having any brothers or sisters. Even before we married Viv talked about the children we would have together, saying her perfect family would be three children. The combination didn't much matter to her except she wanted at least one boy and one girl. Family was important to me, too, but I wanted to wait until we had both graduated from college, worked for a year or two and had established a solid financial footing. Guess who won that argument?*

It was Vivian's contention that God, and God alone, should decide when to bless a married couple with a child. She expressed her inflexible opinion to Trevor on numerous occasions, saying that by using birth control as they did, God's will was being circumvented. Finally, more to appease Vivian than anything, Trevor proposed, "Tell you what; we'll try it one time. If you become pregnant so be it, but if not, you have to agree to wait. We'll start our family at a more opportune time."

Vivian did agree, but she hedged her bet. Attempting to improve her odds of becoming pregnant she consulted a calendar and counted the number of days from her last period. She announced to Trevor the date she had selected to make love without birth control would be the evening of April 25th. Trevor played along and on the afternoon of the impending event he brought home a romantic bouquet of wildflowers he had picked alongside the road. That night Vivian fixed salmon steaks, Trevor's favorite, and she served them with candlelight and soft music played on the phonograph.

That night the dirty dishes were left on the table and Vivian and Trevor retired to the bedroom. They made love and in the afterglow Vivian was almost giddy, she was that sure she had conceived. She snuggled against Trevor's chest and professed, "I do love you. I love you so much."

Trevor told her he loved her too, but secretly he suspected they had made a huge mistake and worried if she did get pregnant they wouldn't be able to pay for the expenses associated with having a child. Complicating the matter even more was Trevor's knowledge that if they did have a baby, Vivian would feel compelled to have more. And nagging at Trevor the way a tongue keeps searching out the gap left by a missing tooth was his fear they were digging themselves a financial hole they could never hope to get out of, not on teachers' salaries.

Vivian did become pregnant. She was four months along when she took her first teaching job at Rockdale Elementary. As her due date drew near one of the worst blizzards in the recorded history of the Columbia Gorge blew in and it snowed every day for a week. And then the wind came up, drifting the snow. Some drifts were 18 feet deep. Travel was nearly impossible. Schools closed. Trevor borrowed the neighbor's tractor and used the blade to plow snow. He plowed eight straight hours and cleared a narrow path from the farmhouse where they were living to the state highway. That evening, January 24, 1950, when Vivian went into labor, he chained up the Desoto sedan and they fought their way through the snowdrifts to the hospital. The following day, after more than 20 hours of labor, during which the baby had to be turned to avoid a breech birth, Nicholas Earle Russell, a beautiful, healthy baby boy was born.

Three days later the mother and child were released from the hospital. Once again Trevor had to work clearing the road with the tractor in order to get his family safely home. And then Trevor worried if there was a medical emergency he would never be able to get the them back to the hospital. His worries proved unfounded. Nick was the ideal baby. And when Trevor held him, or when he watched Vivian nurse, the joy he felt filled him with pride. He told Vivian he didn't believe he had ever been so happy and in return she told Trevor that now, as a mother, she felt *fulfilled*.

*****

In quick succession the Russell family was blessed with two more children: Frank born in 1952 and named after Trevor's father, and 10 months and 28 days after Frank's birth, Patti was born. Trevor, needing to find a better paying job to accommodate his expanding family, applied for the position of principal at Willamette City Elementary, a new school under construction in the town of Oakridge, located at the upper end of the Willamette Valley in the Cascade Mountain Range. The thing Trevor most liked about the area was that it provided ample opportunities to hunt and fish. He also believed it was important to raise his children like he was raised, and to instill in them an appreciation for nature and all that a rural lifestyle has to offer. Vivian was of the same opinion.

Trevor visited Oakridge and met with Paul Elliott, the superintendent. When Trevor was offered the job he asked for time to think about the decision and the opportunity to discuss it with his wife. After the meeting Trevor drove around and appraised the community. Lookout Dam was nearing completion and timber was being cut behind what was to become Hills Creek Dam. The town of Oakridge was bisected by Highway 58 as well as the north/south railroad mainline. It appeared to be a stable community, one that was likely to grow. But what really sold Trevor on taking the job was when he stopped at Salmon Creek and unlimbered his fly rod. It didn't seem to matter which fly he tied on the end of his leader; the hungry rainbow trout inhaled each and every one. He caught so many fish his arms grew weary. He took the 10 largest fish, gutted them, laid them on a bed of grass in his creel and drove to Paul Elliott's house. He presented the fish to the superintendent and said, "I've never caught so many fish, so easily, in my entire life. I'll take the job."

*****

The Russell family moved to Oakridge, and to become better acquainted with the area they took a camping trip up Salmon Creek. It was here Nick was stung by a yellow jacket. His arm swelled to twice its normal size and his throat constricted, making it very difficult for him to breath. He was rushed to the medical clinic in Oakridge where the doctor on call administered a shot to counteract the poison from the sting. Trevor and Vivian were instructed that in the future medication should always be kept close at hand, and they were warned another sting, if untreated, could potentially be fatal to Nick.

Several years later Trevor took Nick and Frank on a hiking and camping trip into the remote recesses of the Cascade Mountain range. They planned to climb Fuji Mountain and Mount David Douglas, and to fish at Bingo, Bongo and Waldo lakes. It was prearranged that, after spending five days camped in the wilderness, Vivian and Patti would pick them up at Gold Lake.

On the second day of the outing, a warm, sunny fall day, Trevor was following a compass bearing toward Bingo Lake, hiking beneath a canopy of stately fir trees. A deer went out in front of them, thump-thump-thumping and breaking off limbs in the thick underbrush. A gray squirrel sat on a branch overhead and chastised them. One of the three hikers stepped on a twig and there was a sudden buzzing. Yellow jackets swarmed from a hole in the ground, moving in unison like a miniature tornado. Trevor was stung on the neck and wildly waved his arm against the malicious insects as he tried to shepherd his boys away. Frank was stung twice. He yelped both times. As they ran Trevor chastised himself because he had forgotten to put the bee sting medication in his pack. He knew if Nick was stung he might die and he pictured Nick in his arms, his little boy fighting for breath, and Trevor thought there could be nothing worse than for a parent to lose a child. His grief at that moment was almost unbearable.

The trio, thankfully, was able to outrun the yellow jackets and Nick was not stung. But as they continued on Trevor was concerned and watchful every step of the way. As a precaution they stuck to the main trails. On the fifth day the hikers came out of the woods at Gold Lake and Vivian and Patti had a picnic lunch waiting for them. While they ate Frank and Nick talked excitedly about the fun they had had. Though he was hungry Trevor felt such an overwhelming rush of relief that his boys were safe that he had no appetite for food. He ate very little. After the food was gone they went home.

*****

Trevor saved up and bought a 12-foot boat with a 7½ horse kicker. The Russell family's next investment, purchased on time, was a 16-foot camp trailer. During the warm weather months, on Friday after school or anytime during the summer, they went camping, oftentimes crossing over the mountains to the High Desert. One of their favorite spots to camp was Bear Flat, a sprawling meadow between Chemult and Silver Lake. The open area allowed Trevor and Vivian to sit in lawn chairs and watch their children play; the boys had BB guns and crawled on their bellies like military commandoes and Patti wandered around looking for interesting rocks.

From an early age Trevor instructed the boys in gun safety. Santa brought them .22 caliber single shot rifles the year they turned 8 years old and they enjoyed hunting jackrabbits, rattlesnakes and sage rats. It was Patti who loved to fish. One time the family was camped near Harriman Lodge on Klamath Lake. The boys were busy searching for arrowheads in the mud where the lake had receded. Trevor and Patti went fishing, trolling for lake trout on Pelican Bay. It was Patti's greatest desire to join the Lunker Club, whose membership required an angler to catch a rainbow trout weighing at least 8 pounds. If she was ever so lucky as to catch a fish that size, she would be given a certificate and her picture would hang on the wall of fame at Harriman Lodge.

Patti saw a big trout leap far behind the boat and she started to point in that direction, but at that precise moment the rod she was holding took a dive and the reel sang as a fish stripped line. "I've got a bite!" she exclaimed. Grabbing for control of the rod she set the hook with a firm upward motion of the tip of the spinning rod.

For nearly 20 minutes Patti fought the wild fish. It made long runs stripping off line, and when it slowed or swam toward the boat Patti reeled, always keeping the rod tip up as her father had taught her to do. While Patti was engaged in battling the fish Trevor maneuvered the boat away from the shore and the tules and out to open water. The big fish began to tire, and as it swam near the boat Trevor asked his 6-year-old daughter, "Do you want to net it?"

"Yes," she replied.

"Sweetie, this is a little different than the fish you've netted for me," said Trevor, his voice was calm and reassuring. "It's a whole lot bigger. You have to slip the net under its tail and bring it up quickly. Once the top of the net is above water, turn it so the opening closes. Hold it there. This fish is too heavy for you to lift it into the boat."

Patti handed the rod to her father and he gingerly played the fish while she picked up the net and expertly slid it under the swimming fish. Trevor lifted the rainbow into the boat and Patti screamed, "I did it!"

That scream brought Vivian on the run, and when the little boat reached the dock and Patti showed off her fish, Vivian said, "I wasn't worried you were drowning – it sounded like a happy scream."

The fish weighed 8¾ pounds. Patti was inducted as a member of the Lunker Club and for many years her photograph with her big fish was proudly displayed on the wall of fame at Harriman Lodge.

*****

"We had ourselves a little accident," announced Vivian one night as she and Trevor lay in bed together with the light on.

Trevor had been reading an article in *Outdoor Life* about hunting whitetail deer in Montana and at first he assumed his wife had been involved in a fender bender and wanted to tell him about it. He set aside the magazine. "Nobody was hurt, were they?"

"Not that kind of an accident," said Vivian in a voice that was very flat and impassive.

Trevor looked at her then. He said, "Oh." That was all he said.

"We can't have this one." Vivian was resolute. "It's not possible. It wouldn't work. It would be too disruptive for our family."

Trevor broached the subject as though he was testing the temperature of the water. He certainly was not willing to jump in and say the word *abortion*. He cautiously asked, "Are you thinking of ending it?"

"I don't want to think that, but maybe it would be best," said Vivian. Silent tears glistened on her cheeks.

Trevor took a tissue from his nightstand and affectionately dabbed away those tears. He said, "Let's talk about this."

"Not now," said Vivian. "I'm too emotional."

"When did you find out?"

"I've known for a while."

"You're sure?"

"A woman knows."

"Have you seen a doctor?"

"No."

"Then how do you know?"

"I missed my last period. I've been sick in the mornings. My breasts are tender. My moods are like a roller coaster, up and down. I'm sure."

But Vivian was not sure about anything. She certainly did not know how she should react to this unanticipated, unwanted pregnancy; and she didn't know how she wanted Trevor to react either. Maybe she wanted him to put his arms around her, tell her how much he loved her and that everything would be all right. But everything was not going to be all right. She didn't want the discomfort and bloating of pregnancy, didn't want the hassle of constantly tending a baby; the feeding and diapers, the disruption to her life and her family's life, the attention a baby required, the demands of a baby. She thought her pregnancy was the worst thing that could have ever befallen her.

*****

Vivian refused to visit a local doctor and potentially have the news of her pregnancy spread around the small town of Oakridge. She asked Trevor to drive her 60 miles to meet a doctor who Vivian had been told sometimes performed illegal abortions. The doctor was a big man who dressed in a white smock and sat behind a metal desk that, except for one small pile of papers, was clean of clutter.

"Tell me why you're here," he requested.

"I'm pregnant and I don't want to be," Vivian said succinctly, and after a moment's pause she began to ramble. "There are a lot of reasons to stop this here and now. We have three children. It's been 8 years since the last one. We just moved into a new house. We are finally starting to get ahead of our bills, and now I'll have to give up teaching and we'll lose that income. I don't have the energy for this. It's the wrong time. We already have our family."

The doctor held up a hand motioning for Vivian to stop talking. He told her, "First let's make sure you really are pregnant. If you are then we can talk about alternatives you might want to consider and the ramifications of each of your options." He addressed Trevor, "Why don't you wait in the car. This won't take long."

Trevor went to the car and for a while he was content to listen to the radio, but it proved nothing more than a mindless distraction and he turned it off. He needed time to think. He wondered if Vivian was going through with what she had planned. That thought worried him, and as a half hour bled into an hour Trevor began visualizing the scene transpiring inside – the doctor with a long, blunt needle, or would he use a suction device, Trevor didn't know – and it was at that point Trevor realized this was not something as simple as an *unwanted pregnancy*. It was a baby, their baby, a baby he could hold in his arms, a baby with pink skin and a smell as sweet as vanilla: a tiny, helpless baby. Was it a son? A daughter? Trevor reflected on the first time he held Nick, and Frank, and Patti. He was smiling at the memories. And he was crying, too.

Overcome by a sudden urge to rush into the doctor's office and holler, "Stop! Stop this thing!" Trevor was reaching for the door handle – might very well have carried through with his impulsive act – but he happened to look in the direction of the doctor's office and saw Vivian marching down the steps. At first glance there was absolutely no way for Trevor to tell what had happened. Her face was as blank as a freshly painted wall. Trevor's instinct was the pregnancy had been terminated and he was gripped with such a graphic fear he actually felt his heart sink in his chest.

Vivian opened the door, slid onto the seat, closed the door and turned to face him. It was then he knew the truth. What he saw in his wife's eyes, those lovely brown eyes he had fallen in love with so many years before at Morlan's Confectionary, told him everything he needed to know. He saw merriment, anticipation, joy. She seemed so full of life, new life, and she was. With firm conviction she told Trevor, "We are going to have this baby."

*****

Vivian was happy all through her pregnancy. She taught until Valentine's Day morning, 1961, when her water broke and she went into labor. A few hours later an announcement was made over the intercom at Oakridge Elementary informing the students Mrs. Russell had given birth to a healthy baby boy, Jeffery Kay Russell.

Patti heard the news over the classroom speaker and burst into tears. The teacher tried to console her. "This is wonderful news. You have a baby brother. Why are you crying?" asked the teacher.

"I wanted a sister," bawled Patti.

*****

The older boys in the Russell family grew up exactly like their father had, spending most of their waking hours when they weren't in school, playing in the outdoors. They hunted and fished, hiked and explored. Nick, the oldest, was the one who stepped up and took charge. He killed rattlesnakes and sage rats and was the one who usually found the perfect arrowheads. Every year he filled his deer and elk tags. Frank was younger, but he was by far the more competitive of the two boys. He felt he had something to prove. One time, when he was just a little tyke, he was standing on the dock at the Siletz cabin fishing for steelhead. He tried to cast to the far side of the river and somehow managed to throw himself over the rail and into the water. He was wearing a life jacket and when he came near the end of the dock where Dan O'Leary, the shop teacher in Oakridge who often came to the cabin to fish was standing, Dan reached down and pulled Frank from the water. Frank was blubbering and Dan thought it was because of the shock of the cold water, but Frank cried, "I lost my pole."

Dan rigged up a heavy weight and a treble hook on his line and retrieved the new rod Frank had received for his birthday. And Frank, even though he was soaking wet and cold, continued to fish. He was that competitive.

After graduating from high school Nick enlisted in the Army, serving in a paratroop division and spending most of his service time jumping out of aircraft. Frank enlisted in the Navy as a radio technician. Patti went to community college, moved to California and got married. By the time Jeff started fourth grade his brothers and sister were gone from home. And because of that Jeff was treated differently than his siblings. The other children had been told, "Don't do that" and they would stop whatever they were doing. Jeff demanded explanations and reasons. He was fun-loving, extremely sensitive, kind and caring. He was smart, curious and contemplative. He was artistic and creative, mechanically minded and he had a unique way of looking at life that he counterbalanced with a terrific sense of humor. Trevor and Vivian thought he was the best kid in so many ways.

Jeff was a mommy's boy. When he was very young Vivian taught him to cook, and in the kitchen they visited like neighbors. They had fun together. But if Jeff was a mommy's boy he was a daddy's boy, too. As soon as he could hike and get around in the woods Jeff hunted with his father, staying a step or two behind, walking so silently Trevor often forgot he had a shadow. One year they were deer hunting in the Cascades and it was a typical gray, foggy, drippy day. Walking along a skid trail Jeff unexpectedly broke the silence, "Didn't you even see him, Dad?"

Trevor turned and Jeff was standing a few feet away, hands on hips, clearly exasperated. "See what?" asked Trevor.

"That big buck," said Jeff. "He had horns way out to here." Jeff held his hands over his head as wide as he could reach.

"Why didn't you let me know he was there?" asked Trevor.

"I was trying to tap you on the shoulder and tell you," explained Jeff, and then looking chagrined he added, "Sorry, Dad. Guess I lost my head and got a case of buck fever."

Trevor located where the buck had been standing and began tracking, hoping to catch a glimpse of the trophy animal, anyway a trophy according to Jeff. They followed the buck for several miles before coming out on a road. Two hunters in a pickup truck approached and Trevor waved them down. He told them, "If you drive us back to camp I'll pour you each a tall glass of ice cold homemade wine."

The hunters said to hop in back. Upon reaching camp Trevor was true to his word, bringing out two gallon jugs of wine. He poured a little wine from the first gallon into a pair of 16-ounce cups and had the hunters sample the wine. Then he poured from the second bottle. After asking the hunters to, "name your poison" he filled their cups with the wine they had chosen.

The hunters mentioned they were from the former reservation town of Chiloquin and went on to say they were

Klamath Indians who were hunting on public land because, as the man who introduced himself as Mike Cole said, "Government took away the reservation and all the deer been shot."

Mike was a big man, standing well over 6 feet tall and weighing close to 300 pounds. Near the bottom of his glass of wine he boasted, "If you ever get to Klamath County and get in trouble just say you're a friend of Mike Cole's. You won't have no trouble."

After they had finished their wine Trevor sent the hunters on their way. As they were pulling away Jeff said, "Dad, maybe we should remember Mike Cole's name."

"Why's that?" responded Trevor.

"Just in case we're ever in Klamath County and get in trouble we might need to mention his name."

*****

The joke was that, as far as the local weather in Oakridge went, there were 10 months of winter and two months of damn poor skiing. In order to get some benefit from the long winters in the Cascade Mountains Trevor bought a snowmobile, and then he bought another for Vivian. Until Jeff was old enough to ride his own snowmobile he was relegated to riding behind one of his parents.

The older children were already gone from home when the Russell family decided to spend one Christmas Eve at a small cabin near Bobby Lake. The snow was deep and fresh. The sky opened up and was clear and the temperature was cold. A thin slice of moon and the Milky Way shone brightly. It was a wonderful night for a snowmobile ride. At the trailhead Trevor and Vivian packed everything they thought they would need and strapped it onto a sled. They had firewood, matches, food, sleeping bags and changes of clothes. When they reached the cabin at Bobby Lake and started to unload they discovered they had forgotten a very important item, a light. The interior of the cabin was dark, and even though Trevor got a fire started in the stove it provided little light because, when the door was open, the stove smoked.

Vivian had fixed sandwiches and they ate those in the dark. They sat around for a while and talked in the dark, were about ready to call it an early night and crawl into their sleeping bags when Jeff reluctantly volunteered he had been given a candle by one of his classmates and had brought the candle along in his pack.

"What are you waiting for?" boomed Trevor. "Get it."

"But I was saving it for a special occasion," said Jeff meekly.

"This is a special occasion," responded Trevor.

*****

Trevor was convinced that if he and Jeff could reach Timpanogas Lake, the headwaters of the middle fork of the Willamette River, early in the spring when the ice first melted they could catch their limits of big trout. This would be the first time for Jeff to make a long ride on his own snowmobile.

They started at daybreak. The snow was firm and fast and going downhill was easy, even though they had to go up and down the moguls where snow had been shed off overhanging branches creating high berms and deep wells. Upon reaching Timpanogas Lake they found open water. They fished all that long, warm day and never got so much as a single bite. Finally they gave up and started for the trailhead.

The snow was punchy, the consistency of granulated sugar, and immediately Jeff had trouble on the moguls, not twisting the throttle handle enough and spinning out before he reached the top. Each time his snowmobile lost traction and came to a stop and Trevor had to go back to help, horsing the snow machine around with brute force and driving it back to the top of the mogul so Jeff could build up enough speed to make it up the next run. And each time Jeff, not giving the machine enough gas, stalled out. Over and over again this happened. Trevor was soaked with sweat and he finally told Jeff, "Son, there's a limit on how much I can do. I'm worn out from lifting your snowmobile. I don't want to have a heart attack. You've got to give it more gas on the upside of the hill. You gotta do it, son."

Tears welled in Jeff's eyes. He said, "Dad, I'm just too big of a chicken."

Trevor slung an arm around his son's shoulders and patiently explained, "I can understand that, son, but just try real hard not to be quite as big a chicken as you've been and maybe we'll make it out of here."

Jeff sat on his snowmobile, gunned the throttle and miraculously made it up the face of the first mogul and the one after that and he kept going. When they reached the trailhead Jeff pulled off his helmet. He was grinning widely and told his dad, "You know, I've been thinking. When you're not quite as big a chicken as you think you are, you can accomplish things you didn't think you could do."

*****

By the time Jeff reached junior high school he was a self-professed class clown. He enjoyed making classmates laugh – that was the devilish side of his personality – and he liked to pull practical jokes. Jeff tested and tormented one teacher in particular. She taught social studies and relied on a world map, pulling down the rolled up map affixed to the wall above the blackboard and pointing to specific locations of current events with a round dowel.

Before her class convened one afternoon Jeff slipped into the room, pulled down the map and taped up a poster of a girl in a skimpy bikini. He carefully re-rolled the map and exited the room, returning a few minutes later with his classmates. The predictable teacher began the class speaking about an event that had occurred in the Philippines. Her back was to the wall as she reached behind her and pulled down the map, setting off a titter of giggles that crossed and re-crossed the room in ripples and waves of laughter. The teacher, confused by the students' reactions, turned and when she saw the nearly naked woman she hastily rolled up the map. "Jeffery Russell, what do you know about this?"

"What makes you think I'd know something?" retorted Jeff defensively.

"Because I know you and this is something you'd pull," said the teacher with an inflated sigh.

*****

At an early age Jeff developed a curiosity about mechanical things and wanted to know how and why they worked. He spent the bulk of his evenings in the basement – Trevor had set up a snowmobile workshop there – taking machines apart and putting them back together. He developed an innate understanding of how machinery functioned and gained additional mechanical experience by working on cars and pickup trucks for friends. He never charged for his labor, only for parts. When Jeff's mechanical aptitude was tested in school he was found to be in the top percentile in the nation.

Jeff seemed able to accomplish whatever he set his mind on doing. One time he decided to tackle the unfinished basement.

He hung sheetrock and put up acoustical tile on the ceiling. When Trevor returned from a weeklong antelope hunting trip to Eastern Oregon and stepped into the basement he was in awe of what had been accomplished in his absence. He turned to Jeff and said, "You did a beautiful job. But how in the world did you know how to hang ceiling tile?"

"It wasn't that hard, Dad," replied Jeff.

*****

When Jeff was a senior in high school he asked a girl to the prom, taking her to dinner in Eugene in the family car, a Cadillac Seville. Driving in town a friend pulled alongside Jeff at a stoplight, raced his engine and motioned for a drag race. The light turned green and both cars leaped forward. Jeff's buddy had the faster car and a block away a policeman stopped him for speeding.

Jeff told his father about the incident and laughed, saying, "That Cadillac really doesn't have a lot of low end. That's the only thing that saved me."

Later that month Jeff graduated from Oakridge High School and because his brothers had both been in the service, Jeff enlisted, taking the diesel mechanic schooling offered by the Army. After he was gone Trevor was detailing the interior of the Cadillac and found a marijuana cigarette. He showed it to Vivian. "I don't imagine this is yours," he said. "I have a sneaking suspicion maybe Jeff isn't the picture of perfection we always thought he was."

*****

After spending two years in the Army Jeff returned home and continued his schooling at Lane Community College, taking additional classes in diesel mechanics and specializing in welding. He found a good job as the mechanic for the Lowell School District's fleet of eight school buses. In 1986 he married Tami Jo Widman at Lake Tahoe, Nevada. They bought a house at 1170 Dondea Street in Springfield, Oregon. Jeff continued to work for the Lowell School District and Tami was employed selling blinds to residential and commercial customers in Lane County.

Trevor and Vivian retired from teaching. Their plans were to spend summers in Oakridge and winters in the Southwest where they had purchased a home in a retirement community near Yuma, Arizona. One late fall day Trevor and Vivian visited Jeff and Tami to give them the keys to their house in Oakridge and go over what needed to be done while they were away. During their visit Jeff and Tami said how much they liked their jobs and that they were looking forward to starting a family. Tami even suggested she might have some big news to deliver before Trevor and Vivian got home from Arizona. Trevor took that to mean his son and daughter-in-law were trying to have a baby and that pleased him. He told Vivian, "I can't wait."

*****

On the last day of November, 1988 the remnants of a passing storm left clearing skies and falling temperatures. Dawn was breaking on Western Oregon as Tami drove Jeff to work in Lowell. She was talking about having friends over for dinner that night and never realized the air temperature had dipped below freezing and patches of black ice were forming on the wet highway. On Pengra Road, only a few miles from the community of Lowell, the car hit one of those patches of black ice, went out of control and Tami was helpless to correct the slide. The car slammed head-on into a Shilo Logging Company crummy with four loggers riding to work. The loggers were not injured, but from viewing the wreckage of the car it did not appear anyone inside could have survived, especially not the driver.

Within a matter of minutes the local EMTs had responded to the scene of the accident. They quickly determined there was nothing that could be done for Tami, she had been killed instantly, and they turned their full attention to Jeff. From outward appearances he seemed fine, with only a few minor scratches on his face caused by flying glass from the shattered windshield. But he was unresponsive and was immediately placed in a cervical collar, immobilized to a long backboard, had a bag valve mask placed over his nose and mouth and high flow oxygen administered. He was rushed by ambulance to McKenzie-Willamette Hospital in Springfield. Emergency room doctors quickly determined Jeff's brain stem had been damaged. He remained unconscious and in a coma.

*****

The doctors who treated Jeff concluded his injuries were non life-threatening and they were optimistic their patient would soon awaken from his deep, dark coma. But he did not. He remained on life support; machines breathed for him, fluids dripped from IV bottles suspended on slender silver stands and fluids accumulated in plastic bags attached to the side of the bed. He was totally unresponsive.

*****

Trevor and Vivian were notified of the dreadful accident; Tami's death and Jeff's hospitalization. They caught the first flight to Eugene and when they walked into the Critical Care Unit at McKenzie-Willamette Hospital and found their son lying in bed, his eyes open, they assumed he had awakened from his coma. Trevor was the first to speak, "Hello, son. We came as quickly as we could."

Jeff did not react. He only stared, blinking occasionally, while machines hummed and pinged and heart beats were recorded as red blips on a silver monitor screen. Vivian reached out and picked up one of Jeff's hands that lay limply on his chest. She squeezed the hand. Jeff squeezed back. This gave Vivian a false sense of optimism that Jeff was responding to her. But there was nothing more, only the continual drone of the machines.

Vivian began to cry, more a whimper than cry, and Trevor took her in his arms and she buried her face against his chest. A tiny Oregon junco landed on the narrow windowsill beside Jeff's bed, cocked its black-capped head and peered inside. Beyond, out in the world, traffic passed silently along G Street and people moved about the routines of their lives. This room where Jeff now lay in suspended animation was not of that world beyond the glass. The machine breathed in. The machine breathed out. Ping. Drip. Ping. Drip. Ping. Drip. The Oregon junco flew away.

Trevor and Vivian sat with Jeff and all the while they fully expected their son to fight his way to consciousness, sit up in bed and exclaim, "Dad, Mom, when did you get here? It's so great to see you!" But Jeff did not awaken. Sometimes he blinked his eyes, and when he did not the nurses administered drops of Natural Tears. Other times Jeff closed his eyelids and that was the worst for Trevor and Vivian. When his eyes were open he seemed alive, but when they were closed he looked dead.

Trevor and Vivian slipped away from the hospital to help make arrangements for Tami's funeral. The following day they attended the tearful ceremony. Family and friends expressed their condolences, saying they were praying for Jeff's speedy and full recovery. Afterward Trevor and Vivian rushed back to the hospital to be with Jeff. Upon the doctors' recommendation they purposely did not mention where they had been, about the accident, or that Tami had been killed. The doctors felt that even though Jeff was in a coma he might be aware of all that was going on around him. It was their opinion Jeff should not expend needless energy grieving for his departed wife; he needed to conserve his strength. That was what the doctors thought and Trevor and Vivian went along with their recommendation.

*****

Every day Trevor and Vivian visited Jeff in the hospital. And every day they squeezed his hand and sometimes he squeezed back in response. But other than that, there was no indication to suggest Jeff might soon recover. The machines did their jobs, breathing for Jeff and feeding him. Dreary days dragged one into the next. The gray skies dripped – typical of Western Oregon winter – and sallow, lifeless light seeped through the window and into Jeff's room. Fluorescent bulbs, emitting a hard, thin light, remained on night and day, a tedious constant in the dismal room. There was certainly no comfort in the artificial light. The room smelled of disinfectant and sour despair. But Trevor and Vivian did their best to invent and infuse the room with a sense of cheerfulness. They spoke gaily of times they had spent with Jeff; snowmobiling, hunting, fishing and baking cookies. And even though Jeff remained unconscious they had to believe he was hearing them and processing their words. They waited. And they hoped. It was hope that sustained them.

Jeff was their baby. He was the one they had not been sure about. The one they made a conscious decision to keep. He had been a wonderful child and he had grown to become such a sensitive and loving young man. His personality sparkled. Everyone loved Jeff. And he had been blessed with mechanical talents, had worked hard to hone those talents and skills. Jeff was the one who could fix any broken machine. And now he was broken and it seemed nobody could fix him.

Sometimes Trevor watched Vivian as she sat on a chair beside the bed, holding Jeff's hand. It broke his heart to see the color gone from her face and the hushed tones in which she spoke, reassuring her son he would be alright and telling him how much she loved him. She promised he would awaken, get better and lead a long and productive life.

At those times, really most of the time, Trevor felt weak and powerless. There was nothing he could do for his son and nothing he could do to ease his wife's suffering. His heart felt as cold and hard as a chunk of Arctic ice. And sometimes, when he was at his lowest, the fickle sun fought through the unruly mass of clouds filling the south-facing room with the shine of faithless brilliance. And in those moments Trevor saw God performing a wondrous miracle with sunlight and yet God refused to heal the lifeless body on the bed. Trevor wanted to know, "Why can't you heal Jeff?"

*****

What could Jeff be thinking lying there in that hospital bed; never saying anything, never giving any outward sign of life? Did he have memories, recollections, dreams? Was he aware of his parents' almost constant vigil? Did he hear what the doctors and nurses said about him? Did he wonder why Tami never came to visit? Was he aware of the passing of time, the changes in the weather, the little Oregon junco that returned day after day to perch on the windowsill, crane its spindly neck, stare into the sterile room and fly away? If Jeff was thinking anything, if he was aware of anything, he gave not the slightest indication of it.

*****

A month passed and one morning as Trevor and Vivian approached Jeff's room a nurse stopped them and said, "I thought you knew, Jeff has been transferred to Valley West Nursing Home."

"Nobody told us," said Vivian bitterly. She had been leaping from one small hope to the next, using them like stepping stones to avoid having to face the murky truth. And now with the hospital transferring Jeff to a nursing home, she saw the hopes she had clung to so desperately were gone. Jeff was not going to get better.

Trevor made a sound of disgust in his throat. His face was blotchy with spots of redness and his eyes flashed angrily. He walked away from Vivian and the nurse, went down the long hallway and stepped into the hospital administrator's office. The administrator looked up at Trevor over the top of his glasses, and rather than be alarmed as he should have been he seemed to take this interruption with a calm indifference, as if this was something he half-expected to have happen.

"You made the decision to move Jeff," Trevor said condemningly, his voice thundering around the office, his words like blows he contemptuously flung at the administrator's face. "I suppose from a medical standpoint you have every right to do that. Let me say this, you and your staff run a fine hospital, you take care of your patients and dispense medication, but as a person-to-person communicator you fail the test. If you worked for me, I'd fire your ass. You're the worst communicator I've ever run into in my entire life. Here you are, in a position of power and you never bothered to talk to us, tell us anything. We walk in to see our boy and he's gone. You shipped him out. You made the decision to warehouse him in a nursing home. You ought to be ashamed of yourself."

Trevor waited for a response. When none was forthcoming he continued, "For the past month we've been here every damn day. You could have said something. You should have met with us and said what you thought. You never did. You left my boy on life support and waited for something to happen; when nothing happened you gave up on him. You could have said, in your opinion, he wasn't going to get better. You could have told us you were sending him to a nursing home to die."

The administrator remained impassive. He did not so much as flinch and Trevor, fresh out of words, of accusations and blame, abruptly left the room.

*****

Valley West Nursing Home, located in south Eugene off Bailey Hill Road, was a quiet and clean facility. Residents mobile enough to travel in their walkers and wheelchairs roamed the long, brightly lit hallways. There was the lady in red. She dressed in red every day and loitered near the entryway, greeting visitors and waiting for a conversation she was not capable of participating in beyond her eager, "Hello." An old woman, her mind swept away in a storm-tossed sea of dementia, sat in her wheelchair and crept along the wall, totally absorbed in running the backs of her fingers over the floral patterns on the wallpaper. Residents with deformed and twisted bodies, and yet sound minds, were there; as were those with intact bodies but lost minds. Tucked away – two beds to a room – were the vanquished legion of immobile residents with fake flower arrangements on night stands, family photos on the wall and stuffed animals propped in chairs like impeccably behaved children. These residents, mouths agape, stared blankly at flickering television screens or saw nothing at all. Some only slept, waiting in tranquil desperation for the end to come. And each day when Trevor and Vivian arrived to visit their son they entered and became a part of this depressing storehouse for the dying.

Vivian did her part to infuse Jeff's room with joy. She picked flowers and brought them to the nursing home – the first lavender crocus that pushed up through the snow, some little buttercups the color of the sun, a spindly wildflower as blue as the summer sky, the tips of bare aspen branches shivering in pale green leaves, puffy gray pussy willows – and placed these symbols of budding new life in a vase near Jeff's bed. Each day she threw out the old and added the new. Jeff remained as he had been since his accident, unresponsive and on life support.

Even though Trevor and Vivian were aware of the sad reality, that their son was probably never going to get better, they wanted Jeff to be evaluated by a team of doctors to determine his long-term fate. And yet the parents uncompromisingly clung to the slim possibility that Jeff would awaken, but even if he never did they vowed to devote the remainder of their lives to caring for their invalid son.

The evaluation team was comprised of three specialists. They spent a day with Jeff conducting a battery of tests, and then they met with Trevor and Vivian to go over the results. They were straightforward in their presentation, saying Jeff was blind in his left eye as a result of the impact of the accident. Trevor and Vivian had never suspected that. And they went on to say Jeff had been unresponsive to each and every test that measured brain activity. They bluntly stated, in their collective opinion, it would be a waste of time and a useless expense, to continue to keep Jeff alive on life support.

"The question you have to ask yourselves is this," said one of the doctors. "Would Jeff want to live like this?"

"No," said Trevor, vehemently shaking his head side to side. "You have to understand this is the first time anyone has ever told us exactly what we face. This is a hard thing for us to take." He looked in Vivian's direction. She was dabbing at her eyes with a tissue. "Just so there is no misunderstanding, so we know for positive, you are telling us our son is brain dead, a vegetable, and that there is no chance he will ever get better. Is that correct?"

"That is correct," said one of the doctors and then he sympathetically added, "We're very sorry. We wish we could give you better news."

"We want the truth. We just need to know," said Trevor. "We do appreciate your candor."

The evaluation team departed and for a long time Trevor and Vivian sat in the conference room in silence, but at length they began to talk about the realities of removing Jeff from life support and donating his organs to others who were in desperate need of them. That gave them a measure of solace; that others would be given new life from this personal tragedy. They felt it was the right thing to do and thought that if Jeff was capable of making that decision, he would want his organs harvested for the benefit of others.

For Trevor and Vivian it was a strange feeling, after four months of blind hope, to finally know the full extent of Jeff's injuries, and to be faced with and have to accept there was absolutely no chance of him recovering. Actually it was a relief for them to know those things and to accept them in their hearts. They had been living moment to moment, praying for a miracle that would never happen, could never happen because Jeff's brain stem had been damaged beyond repair. That day Trevor informed Jeff's attending physician that he and Vivian wished to be proactive in Jeff's treatment and asked that their son's feeding tube be removed. But even with the decision made, Trevor and Vivian still clung to the remote chance that, by removing the feeding tube, Jeff would start taking food that was offered to him and swallowing on his own.

The following day the attending physician approached Trevor in the hallway and said, "I've done some soul searching on your request. In fact I wrestled with it most of the night. I want you to know I have a son and I tried to put myself in your position, tried to think what it would be like, how difficult it would be for me to make the decision you have made. Along toward morning I came to the conclusion I do love my son enough to allow him to die. I have granted your request. The feeding tube has been removed."

*****

On Jeff's last day of life, Vivian came down with the flu and elected to stay home. Trevor went to the nursing home alone. It had been several days since the feeding tube had been removed and no water or nourishment had been administered. Trevor saw no obvious changes in Jeff's appearance. He looked the same. His eyes were open. He seemed comfortable, calm even. Trevor took a seat in a chair beside the bed. He picked up Jeff's hand and squeezed it. Jeff squeezed back in response, just as he usually did – more than likely it was only a reflex action – and then his hand went limp once again.

"Son, I'm going to be straight up with you," said Trevor. He had planned what he would say but now he found it difficult to speak. He paused for a long moment to gather his thoughts. "I need to say some things to you and I want you to listen to me very carefully. We never talked about this in front of you, but now I think you need to know. You were in a terrible wreck. Your car slid on a patch of black ice. Tami was killed instantly. You have been in a coma the past four months. You have fought real hard to come out of it. You are a fighter. You have always been a fighter. I'm very proud of you. But there is no way you can beat this. It's impossible. You can't fix this. The doctors can't fix this.

"Your mother and I made the decision to remove your feeding tube. It was a very difficult thing for us to do, the hardest thing we will ever have to face, but I think it is the only decision we could have made. If there was any hope, any hope at all....

"Your mother wanted to be here today, to be with you, as she has been every day for the past four months, but she came down with the flu and didn't want to expose you or the other residents to her germs. She sends all her love. She loves you very much. You know that.

"Son, I want you to relax, close your eyes and let the end come peacefully. Please close your eyes and get ready to go join Tami. She is waiting for you in heaven."

Jeff did close his eyes and without prompting he did squeeze his father's hand one last time. Trevor didn't stop to consider whether this was an acknowledgement or not. He couldn't deal with that. Not then. He would think about that later. Over and over he would think about that. Now he simply mumbled, "I love you, son" and then his tears came hard and fast.

Later, when Trevor was telling Vivian about the end, she cried and said, "I never got to tell him goodbye."

And Trevor said, "Oh yes you did, I told him goodbye for you."

"Somewhere over the rainbow, bluebirds fly. Birds fly over the rainbow, why, then oh why can't I?"

**– recorded by Judy Garland,
from the movie *The Wizard of Oz*, 1939**

A Thousand Acres

~ *Chapter Six* ~

Viv will not allow me to sugarcoat any of the adversity that has befallen us and our family, and if I try, she stops me, says that's not the way she remembers it. Losing Jeff certainly was the worst thing any parent could ever face. It is a parent's worst nightmare. You never get over the loss of a child. I know, since his death I have carried around a hole in my heart, but every so often some good actually does come from all that grief. It did for us. We were able to use some of the insurance settlement from Jeff's accident to help us buy our ranch in Eastern Oregon. Whenever we are there we feel we are as close to Jeff as we can be. I believe his spirit resides there. But before I tell that part of our story – about the ranch – there is something more I have to relate and this is about my Viv and her insidious Parkinson's disease.

Vivian might pick up a virus at school, a cold or a mild case of stomach flu, and nobody in the Russell family ever knew because she refused to let anyone know when she was sick.

A few years before Jeff's accident Vivian realized she was no longer walking correctly. A person's normal gait is to swing the right arm as the left foot comes forward; and conversely with the left arm and right foot. It is the natural way we move and is related to forward motion and balance. From an early age all humans learn to walk this way. Vivian wasn't doing that. She felt clumsy and at first attributed her condition to nothing more than the aging process.

The first time Trevor noticed the change in Vivian's gait was when they were taking a walk in the woods. He scowled and said, "Viv, you seem to be shuffling your feet and your right arm doesn't swing like it should. Is something wrong? Did you pull a muscle?"

"I don't think so. I'm fine." Vivian made a conscious effort to swing her right arm but she could still not do it correctly. Her stride was herky-jerky and not a fluid, natural way of walking. She mentioned to Trevor in passing that there were times she experienced an odd tingling sensation.

"Where?" asked Trevor in concern.

"I don't know," said Vivian, "kinda all over."

And later, when she had trouble sleeping, seemed restless and noticed her right hand was shaking, Vivian became worried and mentioned her symptoms to Dr. Warren Griffin who lived next door to the Russell family. He asked Vivian to come to his office the following day, and while she was there Dr. Griffin asked if there was any possibility she could have been bitten by a spider.

"Yes," said Vivian. "A few weeks ago I woke up in the middle of the night and thought I had been bitten by something. I turned on the light but couldn't find any spiders or bugs in the bed. A couple of days later I noticed a few little bumps on my neck."

Doctor Griffin was confident Vivian's ailments were from a spider bite; most likely a black widow, brown recluse or hobo spider. He administered a test and when the results were returned to him, Doctor Griffin was forced to rule out toxic poisoning. There was no sign of toxin in Vivian's system.

And still Vivian's symptoms continued and became even more pronounced. When she walked her right arm hung limply at her side. She felt a growing weariness, especially on the right side of her body. It was becoming more difficult for her to talk; it seemed to her as though her tongue was swollen and she slurred some words. There were also times when it was difficult for her to swallow. This progression of symptoms – some were attributed to the stress she felt during Jeff's hospitalization – were of grave concern to Doctor Griffin. He suspected Vivian might have Parkinson's disease, but he didn't tell her that. Instead he referred her to a specialist in diagnosing Parkinson's.

The specialist went through his checklist with Vivian: Do you ever experience shaking in a hand, arm, or leg? Do you have stiff muscles or aching muscles? Have you experienced a reduction in arm swing motion when you walk? Do you feel rigidness in the muscles of your legs, face or neck? Do you feel a weakness of face and throat muscles causing you to slur words? Is it sometimes difficult for you to pull yourself up out of a chair, or turn over in bed? Have you become more dependent, fearful, indecisive, and passive? Have you noticed a change in your handwriting? And after Vivian had answered yes to every single question, the doctor asked her to walk across the room. She did, and when she returned to her chair he declared, "You have Parkinson's disease."

"How do you know?" asked Vivian defensively.

"There is no test that can be administered to confirm Parkinson's," admitted the doctor. "But you have all the classic symptoms and besides, when I watched you walk, I could tell. I've seen enough of these cases to know."

Trevor was upset with what seemed to be the doctor's offhanded diagnosis and voiced his opinion. But Vivian wasn't upset, not at all. She told Trevor, "Well, I knew something wasn't right. At least now we have a name for it."

Trevor went to the public library and read about Parkinson's. He learned it is a disease that mostly afflicts people middle-aged and older and results from the gradual degeneration of nerve cells in the portion of the midbrain that controls body movement. The disease progresses through a series of degenerative steps. Vivian would be facing a future in which she would gradually lose her motor skills, suffer dementia and die. To Trevor it seemed so totally unfair that his loving wife should have to endure the effects of such a threatening disease and when he voiced his opinion Vivian told him, "Life isn't always fair. You should know that."

Vivian was referred to Doctor Nutt, a neurologist and co-founder and director of the Oregon Health and Science University Parkinson's Center. At their first meeting Vivian told Doctor Nutt, "If you ever have an experimental procedure, or an experimental drug, and need someone to act as a human guinea pig, I'd like to volunteer."

Doctor Nutt studied Vivian's face searching for an answer and when none was forthcoming he asked, "And why would you volunteer for something like that?"

"Because I still believe in miracles," said Vivian.

*****

Trevor was born east of the mountains and never had been fond of the west side of Oregon. It was just too green, too wet and there was too much underbrush. The east side with open space, a drier climate and four well-defined seasons was more to his liking.

Trevor had a wild notion to use some of the settlement from Jeff's insurance and buy land in Eastern Oregon. He found a thousand-acre ranch for sale near Post, almost dead center in the middle of the state, and convinced Vivian to go with him and have a look at the property. They drove over the Cascade Mountains, dropped down onto the High Desert and Trevor felt a sense of freedom, a liberation of sorts, as if he was leaving all the troubles of the past behind on the west side. As he drove through the wide panorama of the High Desert – populated with sagebrush, scrub juniper, volcanic rocks and the occasional cow – he thought how Eastern Oregon could be a new beginning.

It all depended upon how Vivian felt about making such a drastic change in their lives. He watched her now out of the corner of his eye. She sat buckled in the seat beside him. Her arms twitched and jerked. She wiggled and squirmed. Her shoulders moved. Her legs jumped. She simply could not sit still. The Parkinson's had progressed that far. Vivian had once been a size ten and weighed 135 pounds. Now she was down to a size zero and weighed 85 pounds. Her weight loss was caused by her constant involuntary movements. She burned up more calories than she could ever take in.

They pulled off the highway and stopped in front of the pair of gas pumps at the store in Post, the only building in town. They bought water and snacks and continued on, turning up Camp Creek Road. When the pavement ran out they kept going. They found the gate leading to the ranch that was for sale and drove up the rutted trail to a little shack that was barely livable. There was also a barn in the process of collapsing in on itself and a sad collection of old machinery, including a 1941 one-ton truck that sat rusting in the weeds. All around was open countryside and incredible silence.

"We can build a cabin," offered Trevor.

"There's no electricity," said Vivian.

"We'll run a generator and use solar," said Trevor.

"It's so far away from anywhere," said Vivian.

"Yes it is," said Trevor. "Isn't it wonderful? And if we bought it, we'd have it all to ourselves. Just listen. Isn't the quiet fabulous? It's like we are the only two people in the entire world."

Vivian looked down. Near her feet she saw a blue feather. With difficulty she forced herself to lean over, and with still greater difficulty she was able to close two shaky fingers around the feather. She brought it near her face. "A bluebird," she said and she smiled. "We have bluebirds on our ranch."

*****

The medications Vivian took did not control, or even slow the cumulative effects and the steady advancement of her Parkinson's disease. Doctor Nutt felt as though experimental treatment might be an option, and since Vivian had volunteered to serve as a human guinea pig he called her in for consultation and outlined the procedure he thought might be an option for her to consider, a pallidotomy.

Doctor Nutt explained that during a pallidotomy a tiny electrical wire is inserted into the patient's brain and heated to 80 degrees Celsius for 60 seconds, thereby destroying a small area of the brain and reducing brain activity in that area. The doctor said if the procedure went perfectly it could help reduce Vivian's constant movements and control her tremors and muscle rigidity.

"What are the risks?" asked Trevor.

"There are many," said Doctor Nutt becoming grave in his demeanor. "Seizures and infections are always possible. There have been instances where a patient suffers bleeding in the brain and this can result in a stroke. If the area to be deadened is not precisely identified, a patient can go blind, suffer memory loss, or experience a radical personality change. We don't know. This is a relatively new procedure."

The doctor turned his attention to Vivian. "I plan to perform pallidotomy procedures on 10 patients. Are you interested in being one of those patients?"

"Yes," said Vivian without hesitation.

Vivian was given a number of MRIs to identify the precise location in her brain for treatment. On the day of her surgery a small area on the left side of her scalp was shaved and a local anesthetic was administered. An elaborate metal device was attached to her head. She was awake – would remain awake throughout the procedure – as she was wheeled into the operating room. Trevor was with her, dressed in a green gown with a green mask over his face. He sat in a chair holding Vivian's hand and watched as Doctor Nutt began cranking the handle of an old-fashioned hand crank drill attached to the metal device that stabilized Vivian's head and kept it from moving. A tiny hole was opened through the thick skull bone and a thin wire, a probe, was inserted in the hole and slowly fed through and into the brain. Through all of this, Vivian's body continued to spasm but her head remained immobilized.

Trevor watched on a television screen as the probe moved inside Vivian's brain. The doctors intently watched the progress too, talking constantly among themselves about the procedure until the precise spot in Vivian's brain was reached and Doctor Nutt announced, "We're there."

Trevor sat rigidly. There was a thin sheen of sweat on his forehead and when he realized he was holding his breath he forced himself to exhale and inhale. Vivian's body continued to convulse, but still she managed to whisper to Trevor, "I'll be okay."

Heat was applied to the end of the probe and instantly Vivian's tremors stopped. Her eyes that had been scrunched shut opened abruptly. Other than that, she did not move. And that was the miracle. She did not move. She waited. She pursed her lips into an O and blew Trevor a silent kiss. From the look of contentment that swept over Vivian's face, the stillness in her body must have seemed heaven sent. Slowly she began to relax and smile, a smile of absolute joy. Doctor Nutt slowly withdrew the wire. The harness was removed from Vivian's head.

"Can you sit?" asked Doctor Nutt.

Vivian sat up without difficulty. She folded her unmoving hands in her lap.

"Can you write your name?" someone asked and Vivian was handed a pad of paper and a pen.

She took the pen, poised the tip over the paper and in a wonderfully fluid motion she wrote her name. Her penmanship was flawless, as beautiful as it once had been. She held it up for all to see. She was laughing.

*****

Vivian told Trevor it was finding the bluebird feather that convinced her they should buy the thousand-acre ranch in Eastern Oregon. She said that feather had been a sign directly from God.

When at the ranch what Vivian most enjoyed was the freedom it allowed her to explore the property and search for bluebirds – although she spotted very few – and to find interesting rocks, flowers, birds and animals. She hunted flowers with a passion, picking the blossoms when they were at their showy best and pressing them between pages in books; placing a note with each detailing the name, date and location where the flower was found.

Vivian tried to make friends with a cottontail rabbit. She named it My Rabbit and when it came hopping into view she patiently waited to feed it bites of lettuce, carrots and celery. The little rabbit, whiskers on his nose twitching, inched closer and closer to Vivian's outstretched hand and would almost take the treat that was offered, but invariably Vivian's arm or fingers involuntarily jerked or twitched and the little rabbit scampered away.

For a brief time the pallidotomy operation had been a wondrous escape from Vivian's symptoms of her Parkinson's disease, but those symptoms were gradually returning, although they were nowhere near as severe as they had been. But the disease was progressing, there was no doubt about that, and yet Vivian remained happy despite her recognition the reprieve was only temporary.

*****

A month after the pallidotomy procedure had been performed, the 10 people involved as patients met in a conference room at Oregon Health and Science University in Portland. Most of the patients had shown only slight improvement. Two were negative. One of those had experienced a drastic personality change. Before the operation he had been very reserved and would never think about saying anything inappropriate. During the meeting he shouted uncontrollably, like a person with Tourette's syndrome will do, and proved such a distraction he had to be removed from the room. Another patient had become so violent after his pallidotomy he was confined to a nursing home and had to be physically restrained.

Vivian was the star of the meeting and when called upon to speak she stood and acknowledged the courage it required for each of the patients to volunteer for the experimental procedure. She explained to the group how lucky she felt with her personal success as a result of the procedure and how joyful it was to finally have some relief from the crippling effects of her disease. She thanked Doctor Nutt and his team of doctors and nurses for their work in advancing the treatment for Parkinson's. And when she sat down the others – the medical staff, patients and their spouses – stood and applauded her.

*****

Sons Frank and Nick, as well as friends from Oakridge, visited the ranch to spend a few days and help with the construction of a cabin. When completed, the two-room cabin featured propane lights and 12-volt lights powered by solar panels and a battery pack. A generator served as a backup on cloudy days. There was a propane stove and propane refrigerator, but the cabin lacked indoor plumbing. An outhouse, painted with whitewash, was available and Vivian called it the Whitehouse. When headed in that direction she would announce, "I'm going to the Whitehouse to visit Hillary."

Vivian loved to sit on the front porch of the cabin and watch the way the sun set behind the Maury Mountains, see the long shadows march across the valley floor and sunlight kiss the top of Logan Butte as a grand finale to the passing of another day. Vivian was sitting on the porch when a pair of mountain bluebirds landed in a nearby tree. The male was a lively blue color, its feathers seemed almost iridescent, and the female was a dusky blue. The female flew away, returning after a few minutes, and then the male repeated the female's actions. Vivian called to Trevor, "I've got two lovebirds out here looking for a home. Why don't you build them a bird house?"

Trevor, using leftover scraps of wood from building the cabin, threw together a bird house. Vivian directed him to tack it to the same juniper tree where she had watched the bluebirds – she called it the bluebird tree – and even before Trevor could fold up the ladder and walk away, there was a brilliant flash of blue. The male mountain bluebird was at the round entrance hole of the bird house. He stuck his head inside and flew away. The female was next, flying to the bird house, looking inside, and then flying away. Almost immediately the birds began alternating, bringing twigs and other material and building a nest inside the bird house. They even pulled apart threads from a remnant of a shag rug that had been tossed over the railing, and used that in the construction of their nest.

Vivian had so many questions that she wanted to know the answers to that Trevor finally went inside the cabin, pawed through a box of books and found the one he was looking for, *"Familiar Birds of the Northwest."* He turned to page 47 and learned from the drawings the birds using the new bird house were mountain bluebirds. He found an article that had been cut from a newspaper and placed between the pages and he read this to Vivian. The article stated bluebirds use twigs, deer hair, horse hair, feathers and even thistle down to build their soft nests.

"And shag carpet too," added Vivian with amusement.

The article went on to say mountain bluebirds typically lay three and sometimes four eggs. The eggs are robin egg blue.

The female is relegated to spending 21 days on the nest – the incubation period – and the male brings her food. Once the eggs hatch, the parents trade off feeding the young.

"According to this article," said Trevor skipping to near the end, "mountain bluebirds mate for life."

"Ah," said Vivian. "That is so sweet. Just like you and me."

Trevor built several more bird houses that spring, making sure to cut the entrance hole exactly 1 and 3/16 inches just as the bird book stated it should be for bluebirds. If the hole was bigger, then starlings, crows, ravens, magpies and other predatory birds could stick their heads inside and kill the baby bluebirds. A second pair of mountain bluebirds did occupy another of Trevor's new bird houses and several wrens and nuthatches moved into others.

Vivian watched the first pair of mountain bluebirds raise their young. They had three offspring. One by one the babies left the nest and flew away. Vivian made Trevor promise that during their winter vacation to Yuma, he would build more bird houses and they would put them up around the ranch to encourage even more bluebirds. It was Vivian who suggested they put a sign over the gate to the entrance of the ranch. She wanted it to read, *Bluebird Valley Ranch.*

*****

Not long after the family of mountain bluebirds departed the nest in the front yard, a friend Trevor and Vivian had first met in Yuma came to the ranch for a visit. Aubrey had had a long career in the Hollywood film industry and he had always lived in a city, or when he traveled he stayed in his motor home in a recreational development. He shook his head at the bigness of the landscape at the Bluebird Valley Ranch and stated he would love to go for a walk but was deathly afraid he might become lost.

"You can't get lost," Trevor assured him. "You can always see Logan Butte, that big point over there, and if you stay in this valley and don't go over any mountains you sure as hell won't get lost." Trevor laughed at the very idea of someone becoming lost. To him it seemed ludicrous.

Aubrey did go for a walk, and he did become lost. He panicked and began yelling for help. Trevor heard the cries and found Aubrey headed over the hill toward the next valley. Aubrey vowed he would never venture away from his motor home again, and he never did.

*****

Trevor developed a dryland golf course on the ranch property. It was located in the draw below the cabin. When friends came to visit – most had motor homes or trailers – they played golf and drank beer or had mixed drinks. Even Vivian was able to play golf; at least for a while she did, until the symptoms of the Parkinson's disease returned and robbed her of that ability.

Vivian had taken 10 golf lessons from a professional golfer in Yuma. Because of her tremors she was unable to place the ball on a tee but she could still swing the club. One time Vivian wanted to play golf at the ranch and Trevor set the ball on the tee for her. Vivian hit the ball straight and true, but she could not keep herself upright and unceremoniously fell on her behind.

"You hit that really good," complimented Trevor.

Vivian got to her feet and dusted herself off. She requested of Trevor, "Please set up another." She hit this ball as well as the first, but once again she fell.

"You hit two really good shots," said Trevor.

"I did," said Vivian. She got up off the ground. "And I think it's time I quit the game."

*****

Vivian was invited to her 50th high school reunion but said she didn't think she wanted to go, claiming she would feel uncomfortable having old friends see how the return of her Parkinson's was affecting her. "I don't want their sympathy, or their pity," she told Trevor.

But Trevor convinced her she should go, telling her, "We'll have a great time."

Bud Foster, who had been the senior class president, was the master of ceremonies that night. He introduced Vivian and highlighted her high school accomplishments, saying she had been the annual editor, newspaper editor and was at the center of every school event or happening.

"All of us guys were in love with Vivian Richardson," admitted Bud. He tossed a nonchalant wink in Vivian's direction and added, "I know I certainly was."

He went on, "After graduating from Dallas High School, Vivian attended the University of Oregon and majored in journalism. We expected her to come home and run the *Itemizer/Observer* for her father, maybe win the Pulitzer Prize, or write a book that reached the top of the *New York Times* Best Seller List. But then this out-of-towner, this big tall interloper from the east side of the mountains, Hood River County to be specific, rides in on a white stallion and literally sweeps Vivian off her feet. We didn't know anything about their romance until we read in the newspaper they were married."

Bud turned his attention toward Trevor. "Mr. Trevor Russell, I just want you to know, you stole the belle of the ball."

Trevor beamed proudly. "I know I did," he stated loudly and reached over, picked up Vivian's trembling hand and held it tightly.

*****

Three years in a row, on the 14th day of May, a pair of mountain bluebirds returned to the bird house in the yard at Bluebird Valley Ranch. Vivian said they were the same birds each year because she claimed she recognized their personalities. The following year, the fourth year, the birds arrived on schedule and the female flew to the bird house opening and backed off. The male did the same thing. Then they flew away. Vivian could not understand their unusual behavior and kept watching the opening of the nest. Presently she saw a pair of tiny black noses appear in the hole of the bird house, and then she knew. A chipmunk had taken over the nest and was raising her young there.

There were half a dozen bird houses scattered around in trees and visible from the front deck and Vivian watched them all. Trevor found a rusted out canteen in the hills and wedged it into a crotch in one of the trees. A pair of wrens built a nest inside the canteen and Vivian reported to Trevor what the birds were doing, and when each of the babies left the nest and learned to fly.

One day Vivian was sitting on the front porch and she told Trevor, "If there is such a thing as reincarnation, I'd sure like to come back as a bluebird."

*****

Deer season always brought a small crowd of hunters to the ranch. Trevor and Vivian's sons, Nick and Frank, could be counted on to attend, as well as a handful of friends. One of the stalwarts was Nick's son, Ryan. He was tall and wiry and seemed a carbon copy of his grandfather, back when Trevor had been a young man. Ryan loved to hunt and had forged an extremely close relationship with his grandparents.

One evening, the night before the opening of deer season, the group was sitting around the cabin drinking beer and swapping stories. Vivian was in her wheelchair – by then she was mostly confined to the wheelchair – enjoying the camaraderie of the men. Vivian suddenly interrupted a story, exclaiming, "There's a bird in here!" She flailed her hands as the imaginary bird fluttered near her face.

Vivian was obviously hallucinating and the men, not knowing what to do, threw furtive glances between each other and did nothing, said nothing.

"It's over there," claimed Vivian, now pointing to the far side of the room.

It was Ryan who leaped to his feet and ran toward the corner while waving his hands as if he was attempting to catch the bird.

"There it goes," shrieked Vivian, extending her shaky right arm and waving it down the length of the wall.

Ryan followed, and when he reached the far corner he made a grand display of cupping his hands around the nonexistent bird, exclaiming, "I got it," and directing, "Somebody open the door and I'll turn it loose outside."

After the little drama had transpired, and the men had gone back to drinking and swapping stories, Trevor asked Vivian what type of bird it had been. She replied, "A bluebird, of course."

*****

Over the years I have tried to keep myself in shape with a daily exercise routine. Even before I get out of bed I lie on my back and perform 50 leg crosses, and I do the same with my arms, swinging them wide. I roll onto my shoulders, propping up my behind with my arms and elbows, and pump 300 times like I was riding a bicycle. I take 10 deep breaths and do 10 crunches, trying to tighten all the muscles in my belly. And then I get out of bed and do 50 deep leg squats. After all that I have to sit and rest for a few minutes. Later I play golf or just walk. My goal is to get in at least a mile a day.

One of the reasons I have been so diligent about maintaining my health is I want to take care of Viv as long as I can. Friends tell me I should put her in assisted living, but after having spent time with Jeff in such a facility I resist even the thought of doing such a thing. Viv wants to be home with me. She has told me exactly that on many occasions. It might not always be easy, but I want her to have comfort and joy and if she finds those things at home, then that is where she will remain.

This year we left the ranch in early November and are once again spending the winter here at the home we bought in Yuma. I hired a Mexican woman to help me with Viv and she has been a godsend. Earlier today she drove Viv downtown in the golf cart and Viv bought two new dresses. That is unusual, for Viv to go shopping, but we have a dinner party to go to tonight that she is looking forward to attending. Many of the friends we have made here over the years will be there.

Viv even modeled the dresses for me. I liked both of them, but Viv wanted my opinion on which one looked the best on her and finally I told her the blue one did. She announced that was the one she shall wear to the dinner. She was so pleased with herself.

After trying on the dresses Viv seemed drawn and tired. I suggested she lie down and take a little nap before the festivities. She said she would if I joined her. I did. We lay side by side.

I held her to me. She had a hard time getting comfortable. I whispered, "I love you."

"I love you, too," she whispered back. She tilted her head up toward me and smiled.

I don't know why I chose that particular moment to pose a question to her, but I did. I think one of the reasons was that lately Viv and I had become acutely aware of the fact our time together is drawing to a close. I asked, "Sweetheart, after you're gone and you're in heaven waiting for me, is there anything I can do for you here on earth?"

Her answer was quick and decisive, as if she had already given that particular question considerable thought. She said, "Yes. Promise me one thing; promise me you will bring the bluebirds back to Oregon."

"I promise," I said, quickly adding, "Now will you go to sleep?"

"Okay," she whispered. "Just remember, you promised."

"I won't forget," I stated.

And then she began to relax. She stopped wiggling and squirming. And when I was sure she was sleeping soundly I slowly eased my arm from under her shoulders and sneaked from the room. There were a few things I needed to accomplish before dinner.

An hour or so later, when I went to check on her, Viv had passed on. I sat with her then and thought back to our last conversation. At the time I gave my promise – to bring the bluebirds back to Oregon – I didn't know how I was going to accomplish such an enormous feat. But as I sat with her, holding her hand and feeling the warmth of life slowly ebb from her body the solution came to me as a sudden revelation. I would build bird houses for bluebirds.

*****

Life is never easy for any of us. I have my own health issues: two knee replacements, arthroscopic surgery on my left shoulder, a back operation, double hernia and cataracts removed from both eyes. I wear hearing aids so I can hear. But probably my most troublesome worry is the series of little strokes I've suffered. The doctors refer to them as TIAs and explain an artery inside my brain, the blood source to my brain, is 100 percent blocked. The only reason I'm even alive is other vessels and capillaries have formed to bypass the blockage. But these are narrow and if anything in the bloodstream happens to block one of these passageways, I suffer a small stroke. I realize this is a pretty tenuous situation. They say the next one might kill me, and it might.

I plan on taking whatever time God allows and use it to enjoy life, and to work hard to fulfill my promise to Viv. To date I have built and put up 1,192 bluebird houses. The bird houses are scattered around the countryside; on wooden fence posts, in trees, wherever I can find a spot; and I give away bird houses to anyone who promises to put them up.

It's been a few years now since Viv's passing – we scattered her ashes at the ranch – and I am beginning to see the difference my efforts at building bird houses have made. The bluebirds are definitely making a strong comeback. Each time I see a bluebird I think back to a conversation Viv and I had about reincarnation. A romantic string in my heart goes plunk, and although I know it is highly unlikely, I have to wonder if that bluebird I'm seeing just might be Viv returning to me.

~ The End ~

Epilogue

Grandma Vivian was a very special lady. She was reserved and quiet, never the center of attention but always a part of the action. She loved to cook and sew and I know, after she came down with Parkinson's, it was difficult for her to not be able to do the things she wanted to do. But despite that, and the pain she endured because of her disease, she was always smiling. And that is how I see her now, smiling at me.

Grandpa Trevor is my idol. That man has backbone and conviction. He stands up for what he believes, has never backed away from anything in his life, and he has been up against some tough times. As far as I'm concerned he is a modern day American hero.

Grandpa has always been there for me. He gives me good advice, always has and never tells me what I should do, but points me down the right path. Back when I was in my twenties I started running with the wrong crowd. Grandpa explained to me I was headed down a dead end road, and one day I grew up and quit running with that crowd.

Grandpa taught me to take responsibility for my own actions. Seeing what he did for Grandma, how he treated her with so much love and respect, made a huge impression on me. And now any time I come up against something and have to make a decision, I ask myself one question, "How would Grandpa handle this?"

My grandparents had a wonderful relationship. They truly did love each other. It was a love that lasted over many decades. And after Grandma died and Grandpa started making bird houses, and he told me why he was doing it – because of a promise given – I was blown away. I think the fact he has made over a thousand bird houses shows a lot about his level of commitment and his love for Grandma. It truly does.

I've seen Grandpa with his fake knees climbing a ladder to hang a bird house in a tree 20 miles from the nearest town. It's not easy for him. I try to help whenever I can. Here awhile back I called him and said, "Grandpa, lately I've been giving it considerable thought and I know at your age, and with your health related issues, you're not gonna live forever. I'd like to be able to continue your legacy of making bird houses after you're gone. I hope you feel okay with that." There was a long pause. Finally Grandpa spoke and said he guessed that would be fine. I could tell from his reaction he felt touched by my offer.

When I was at the ranch, it used to be I'd see a mountain bluebird every once in a great while, but we started putting up bird houses and now I see bluebirds everywhere. Sometimes, especially during deer season, there will be huge flocks of bluebirds gathering to migrate south. It's the wildest thing to witness something like that. If everyone followed suit and put up bird houses in their backyards our world would be filled with songbirds.

Just the other day Taylor, my 10-year-old daughter said something to me that really hit home. She said, "Daddy, after Grandpa is gone, and after you're gone, I guess I'll be the one building and putting up bird houses for bluebirds."

Ryan Russell

Bluebird of Happiness

(verse)
The beggar man and his mighty king are only
diff'rent in name,
For they are treated just the same by fate.
Today a smile and tomorrow tears,
We're never sure what's in store,
So learn your lesson before too late, so

(refrain)
Be like I, hold your head up high,
Till you find a bluebird of happiness.
You will find greater peace of mind
Knowing there's a bluebird of happiness.
And when he sings to you,
Though you're deep in blue,
You will see a ray of light creep through,
And so remember this, life is no abyss,
Somewhere there's a bluebird of happiness.

Life is sweet, tender and complete
When you find the bluebird of happiness.
You will find perfect peace of mind
When you find the bluebird of happiness.
Two hearts that beat as one,
'Neath a new found sun,
We are in a world that's just begun,
And you must sing his song, as you go along,
When you find the bluebird of happiness.

**Bluebird of Happiness, written by Edward Heyman and
Harry Parr Davis, sung at Radio City Music Hall
by Jan Peerce, 1934**

Mountain Bluebirds
Facts & Information

- Three species of bluebirds are found in North America. Eastern bluebirds range primarily between the Atlantic Seaboard and the Rocky Mountains. The male eastern bluebird has a bright blue back, reddish-brown sides and a nearly white belly. The coloration of the female is similar, although paler than the male. Western bluebirds have deep blue backs and reddish-brown bellies. They live at low elevations from the Rocky Mountains to the Pacific Coast, and wander the forests and open spaces in search of seeds, insects, berries and fruit. Mountain bluebirds have thin beaks, live at high elevations throughout the West and are easily recognizable by their strikingly iridescent sky-blue plumage. They often gather in great flocks as they migrate south to Mexico during the winter months.

- Poets and songwriters have long held bluebirds close to their hearts and often portray them as romantic symbols of love, renewed hope and happiness.

- The song of the mountain bluebird is typically a rapid, chirping warble, but on occasion they sing for extended periods, especially during early mornings and late afternoons.

- When feeding on insects, a mountain bluebird will hover over an area and pounce on its prey, moving to a perch or nest to feed.

- Mountain bluebirds are believed to be monogamous.

- Mountain bluebirds can be attracted to bird houses placed in open spaces away from predators. Birdbaths and mealworm are also bluebird attractants.

- Big storms during spring and fall can blow migrating birds from their intended course. Lone mountain bluebirds have been reported wandering as far north as the Arctic Circle and into states along the Eastern Seaboard.

- The mountain bluebird is the state bird of Idaho and Nevada. In 1929 a number of women's groups launched a campaign to adopt the western tanager as the official state bird of Idaho, but school children united and appealed to the legislature, convincing the lawmakers to list the mountain bluebird as the official Idaho state bird. Nevada recognized the mountain bluebird as their official state bird in 1967.

- Mountain bluebirds migrate north in early spring, establish territories and select a nesting site. The female lays three or four blue eggs and is relegated to spending 21 days on the nest – the incubation period – during which time the male brings her food. Once the eggs hatch, the parents trade off feeding the young.

- Chimalis (perhaps pronounced SHI-mah-lees) is a Native American word for bluebird.

- One of the most ambitious efforts of bluebird conservation was the development of the National Bluebird Trail in 1938. Garden clubs took up the cause and spread bird houses along highways from coast to coast. Within a decade nearly 7,000 bird houses had been erected, but it was soon discovered automobiles were responsible for killing many bluebirds, and when interest in maintaining the bird houses waned, the trail was abandoned.

- From the starling's introduction to the East Coast of North America in the 1890s, it took only 50 years for them to reach the West Coast. Today the starling population in North America is estimated to exceed 200 million, and because of their aggressive nature they threaten other nesting song birds and are listed as an *invasive species*.

- On March 24, 1963 the popular television series *Lassie* aired an episode in which Timmy, after discovering the bluebird population is declining due to a lack of adequate nesting sites, begins building bird houses. His plans fail when a huge flock of starlings take over the bird houses and neighbors kill the offensive birds with dynamite.

- In the 1960s the Audubon Naturalist Society and the Maryland Ornithological Society combined forces and launched a bluebird project. Over 3,000 bird houses were established and maintained over a 12 year period. It was estimated nearly 30,000 eastern bluebirds were fledged from these bird houses.

- The world's largest trail of bluebird bird houses is located in Canada and stretches nearly 2,000 miles from Ontario to British Columbia.

- Al Emmons was a home owner at the Bluebird Court development in Greendale, Wisconsin. In honor of the namesake of the development he erected a giant bluebird on the chimney of his residence. The Village Historic Preservation Board objected, ordering Emmons to remove the bluebird or face a $100 a day fine. Rather than comply, Emmons painted an American flag on the bird's outstretched wings and there were no more complaints from the Board.

- During his lifetime, Jack Finch is credited with building more than 60,000 bluebird bird houses. At one time he was monitoring 2,000 bird houses across Virginia and North and South Carolina. He died in 2006 at the age of 89.

- The most significant factor in the population recovery of bluebirds has been through the efforts of volunteers – people like you – doing their part by putting up and monitoring bird houses. You can help by encouraging family and friends to get involved in building and maintaining a few bird houses. If all nature lovers contributed to this cause the face of our environment would change for the better, and once again the sweet melodies of song birds would spill across the countryside.

Book Club
Study Guide Questions

How does having been raised in a rural environment affect Trevor Russell in his later life? What personality traits are revealed by Trevor's upbringing? Why did Trevor's brother think it was important for Trevor to stand on his own two feet?

Can you understand the empathy Trevor is experiencing, and the implications he feels for his Japanese American friend, after the outbreak of World War II? What are your feelings about the detainment and relocation of Japanese Americans during World War II?

What is revealed about Trevor when he is confronted by the realities of the situation at Rosie's Café? Do you think Trevor was trying to reclaim his masculinity by having a drink at a bar after his encounter at Rosie's Café?

What does Trevor realize about himself when he breaks up with Betty? Was Betty entirely to blame for the breakup of their relationship? Is Trevor's hesitation about becoming involved with another woman the correct decision?

Was the meeting of Trevor and Vivian a case of "love at first sight" and do you believe such a thing is possible?

How does Trevor view his college roommate, Rollie? What does Rollie's new car represent to Trevor? How does Trevor overcome his roommate's intentions to date Vivian? How does Trevor win Vivian's heart?

When Trevor opened the cans of vegetable soup, did Vivian handle his breach of table manners correctly? What did Vivian see in Trevor's character that appealed to her? Did Vivian do the right thing by breaking up with her fiancé?

What was your response to Trevor helping to fell the maple tree? Why did Trevor choose the baseball field to make love to Vivian? What was the significance of Vivian having changed her majors from journalism to education?

Why did Trevor and Vivian decide to elope rather than be married in a traditional ceremony? How did you feel about the way Vivian's father learned they were married and how could the couple have handled the situation in a more suitable manner?

What was revealed about Trevor and Vivian's personalities when they agreed to take Rollie in as a roommate?

Why did Trevor think it was important to raise their children in a rural environment and what are the advantages and disadvantages to such a decision?

Did Vivian make the correct choice to not terminate her pregnancy and to carry her baby to term? How do you feel about a woman's right to have an abortion?

How was Jeff unlike the other children in the Russell family? Was Jeff treated differently? What was revealed about Jeff after he went in the service?

How would you react if one of your children was seriously injured in an accident? What does the little bird sitting on the windowsill of Jeff's hospital room represent? Do you condone Trevor's reaction when he learned his son has been transferred to a nursing home? What did Vivian do to try and infuse Jeff's room with hope?

What was Jeff's attending physician's reaction to removing life support and how did he verbalize that decision? How difficult would it be emotionally for you to remove life support from a loved one?

What was Vivian's reaction to the news of her son's death? Do you feel the stress Vivian experienced while her son was on life support might have exacerbated her Parkinson's disease? How did Vivian cope with the diagnosis she had Parkinson's disease, and how did Trevor deal with the news? How did Vivian reconcile the woman she used to be, with the woman she had become?

Why did Vivian volunteer for a pallidotomy and did the possibility of relief from the symptoms of Parkinson's outweigh the risks? Can you imagine Vivian's elation after the operation when her symptoms had ceased? How difficult would it be to endure the slow return of the disease? The public is often ill-informed about the consequences of a disease like Parkinson's. What did you already know about the disease, and what insights did you gain from reading "*A Promise Given*"?

What did buying the ranch in Eastern Oregon represent to Trevor? What one thing changed Vivian's mind about purchasing the property? Why did Vivian gain such enjoyment from watching the bluebirds? Why did she want to be reincarnated as a bluebird?

What did Vivian's hallucinations reveal about the advancement of her Parkinson's disease? Why did Trevor refuse to send Vivian to live in an assisted living facility? How would you react if faced with having to make a similar decision?

Was Trevor trying to show Vivian his love for her when he asked the question about what he could do for her after she was gone? What was the significance of Trevor's promise? Discuss your reaction to Vivian's death and the way Trevor handled the situation.

Do you admire Trevor for fulfilling his promise? Do you feel the return of the bluebirds will be Vivian's lasting legacy? How do you feel about the grandson and great-granddaughter's willingness to carry on that legacy?

What segment of "*A Promise Given*" struck a resounding cord for you and why did it?

Do you consider Trevor to be a hero? Who are your heroes and why are they your heroes? How do our heroes reflect our values?

Since *"A Promise Given"* explores a lot of dramatic situations and reveals powerful emotions within us, has reading it changed you in any way? What was the most important thing you learned and what was your strongest reaction and emotion? Would you recommend this book to a friend?

Can you see things that you can do in your normal life to bring about change in your environment? Are you willing to put up a bird house for bluebirds and other songbirds, and are you willing to encourage others to do the same?

Rick Steber, the author of more than thirty books and sales of more than a million copies, has received national acclaim for his writing. His numerous awards include the Western Writers of America Spur Award for Best Western Novel, Independent Publishers Award – Best Regional Fiction, Western Heritage Award, Benjamin Franklin Award, Mid-America Publishers Award, Oregon Library Association Award and Oregon Literary Arts Award. Two of his books have been optioned to movie production companies.

In addition to his writing, Rick is an engaging Western personality and has the unique ability to make his characters come alive as he tells a story. He has spoken at national and international conferences and visits schools where he talks to students about the importance of education, developing reading and writing skills, and impressing upon them the value of saving our history for future generations.

Rick has two sons, Seneca and Dusty, and lives near Prineville, Oregon. He writes in a cabin in the timbered foothills of the Ochoco Mountains.

Reviewers Say...

"Rick Steber has given us a fine example of how fiction can tell the grim facts of history in a highly readable novel. *Buy the Chief a Cadillac* is one of those books which should be added to the reading lists of students of American history."

(Tony Hillerman)

"Steber's words remind you of Hemingway or Fitzgerald...."

(LA Times)

"Rick Steber captures beautifully the mood of the times and of the sturdy people who lived it."

(St. Louis Post-Dispatch)